STORIES FROM GREEK HISTORY

MYTHS AND LEGENDS

STORIES FROM GREEK HISTORY

MARGUERITE DESMURGER

Adapted and translated from the French
by Barbara Whelpton

Illustrated by Jacques Pecnard

A HOLLY BOOK
THE WORLD PUBLISHING COMPANY
CLEVELAND AND NEW YORK

A HOLLY BOOK

PUBLISHED BY THE WORLD PUBLISHING COMPANY
2231 WEST 110TH STREET, CLEVELAND 2, OHIO

Library of Congress Catalog Card Number: 65-24733

Copyright © BURKE PUBLISHING COMPANY Ltd. 1963
Translated from *Récits tirés de l'histoire grecque* (*Contes et légendes* Series)
© LIBRAIRIE FERNAND NATHAN 1962

Stock No. 2712
GB765

Printed in Great Britain

Contents

PART THREE

Stories of Pericles, Alcibiades, Socrates and Demosthenes

PART FOUR

Stories of Alexander the Great

List of Colour Plates

PART ONE

STORIES OF LOCRIS, PROTIS, KUPSELOS, SPARTA AND CROESUS

I

Two Heads are Better than One

"RIEND, where do you come from?" the man from Argos asked his neighbour.

"I come from Locris," replied the other laughing.

The July sun was blazing hot in the stadium at Olympia. The blinding light reflected from the limestone was dazzling wherever the crowd thinned out and exposed a few feet of masonry. Not far off could be seen the façade of the Temple of Zeus.

The wrestling matches were coming to an end; there were only two more pairs of competitors left. The victor would take back to his native city not only a simple wreath of olive leaves but eternal glory.

Who would the winner be? Would it be the athlete of Sicyon whose huge body cast such an enormous shadow? Or could it be one of the athletes from the overseas colonies in Italy? Young Milo of Crotona, with the astonishingly thick muscles, was said to be able to pull apart the trunk of a tree, and to bend a bronze coin between his finger and thumb, just as a child would break a twig.

Whilst bets were being made, the spectators had time to stretch their legs. Little boys ran through the crowd selling cups of water or wine, and dishes of olives and bread. Three men, seated in the strip of shade made by the base of a statue, talked languidly in the heat.

"Our friend here," continued the man from Argos, pointing to his neighbour on the left, "is from Miletus in Asia Minor. He says that it is a lovely town and that he sells purple dye." Then he turned his head and asked, "It is a profitable trade isn't it?"

The Milesian was sweating hard. He was a very stout man and was protecting his head with a little sunshade. "If the dye trade were in a bad way, I shouldn't be here, my good friends," he sighed in a hollow voice. "The journey across the sea is expensive, but every Greek citizen must attend the Olympic Games at least once in his lifetime. I have always said so to my wife," he added, stretching out a hand as big as a plate. "And what makes us superior to the Barbarians? Our Greek blood, of course. Where do the Greeks meet every four years like a band of brothers whether they come from the east or from the west? At Olympia, of course. For such a sacred ceremony even wars cease, and the soldiers on both sides hang up their shields in order to take part in the Olympic Games. Well, every Greek has to come here in order to feel thoroughly Greek, blessed by Zeus, and protected by Hera, so here I am. My brother will look after our factory and the stock will continue to increase just as if I had never gone away. That is why Demagoras of Miletus can

manage to come to the Olympic Games! I owe it to myself and to the gods!"

"So you come from Locris," continued the man from
Argos, turning to his right-hand neighbour. "That's in
southern Italy isn't it? Then you are a neighbour of Milo
of Crotona. Italy must be a splendid country surely;
plenty of wood, wheat, fat cattle, everything you need to
live in comfort. Here in Greece we have to strain every
muscle to try to get more from the soil than it can produce naturally. I don't blame you at all for settling in
Italy, my friend."

"I don't deserve any credit for that," replied the other
cheerfully. "I was born in Locris, like my father, my
grandfather and his grandfather. We are descended from
the people who founded the colony six or seven genera-
tions ago, leaving the Locris in Greece, and founding the
town to which they gave the same name in memory of
their fatherland."

"If I'm not mistaken," continued the man from Argos,
delighted, "a rather funny story is told about that foun-
dation. Do you know it? If you do, you might tell it now
to pass the time away."

"Of course I know it, my dear fellow. It all happened
at a period when the Greeks were scouring the seas in
order to find new places to live in. Times were very hard
then; the rich oppressed the poor, and it looked as if the
soil of our native Greece was so accursed by the gods that
it was refusing to feed the inhabitants. When there is a
shortage of food, people are apt to quarrel. There was
trouble everywhere—rioting and revolutions; those who
could not make their way fitted out ships and placed
images of the gods of their city on board, and off they

went wherever the wind carried them. The lucky ones were those who knew exactly where they were going. They might have been told by some old sailor, or by one of those traders who sell pots and jars all over the Inland Sea, about some fine country across the waters, where there was plenty of space, good soil and climate, and natives who did not know how to fight!

"So those of our people of Locris who were really hard up, left their city. They knew that if they sailed towards the setting sun they would come upon a big island, shaped like a triangle. This island is our Sicily. Even before they reached it, they would find Italy, a rich and untouched land, inhabited by a lot of savages. Already the Greeks who had settled at Naxos, Syracuse and Cumae, beckoned them on.

"Our ancestors landed on the cape which we call today Cape Zephyrion. The natives, poor devils called Siculi, were quite well armed but did not do the newcomers any harm at first. The fact was that our group had to put up with the worst bit of the country. Cape Zephyrion is useless, except to provide grazing for goats and work for stonebreakers. It didn't take the Locrians long to find that out, especially when they looked to the north where there were lovely hills covered with olive groves and wheatfields—the sort of land to tempt anybody.

"But the Siculi began to get awkward when there was a talk of sharing up. 'This land is ours,' they said, 'and we are going to stay on it.'

"Then the Greek leader—a very cunning fellow—went over to the Siculi and made them a jolly fine speech. What was the good of fighting, he asked, when everything could be settled in a friendly way? The Siculi ob-

viously had too much land, since they left half their fields
uncultivated. The Greeks would take the surplus—the
land which was of no use to anybody—and everyone
would live happily side by side, sword in scabbard, sleeping the sleep of the just.

"The native chief remained suspicious. He did not
like the Greek swords, nor the sharp-pointed daggers.

"'And,' said he, 'as soon as we have turned our backs
on you, out will come your swords!'

"'I give you my word,' replied the Greek.

"'I know all about your word.'

"'Well let's swear a solemn oath, one of those oaths
which even the gods would find binding. Let us swear to
remain on good and friendly terms as long as we have the
same soil under our feet and the same heads on our
shoulders. May Zeus' thunderbolt crush me if . . .'

"'All right, all right,' said the Siculus who had
allowed himself to be tempted. 'Let's arrange a meeting
and we'll take the oath.'

"And the day after the ceremony, without any delay,
the Locrians attacked the Siculi, when they least expected it, and drove them back into the mountains. As for
the Greeks, they settled down in the good land and got
the best of everything."

"Well, that's what I call a really scandalous story!"
blurted out the Milesian, deeply shocked. "What did the
gods do about that? If you break an oath, you get
nothing but misfortune."

"But they did not break their oath. That's the whole
point of the story," said the man from Locris.

"I don't see how you make that out," answered the
Greek from Asia Minor.

"Well, the day they took the oath, the Locrians had filled their shoes with earth and, on their shoulders—but hidden under their cloaks—they had placed heads of garlic."

The man from Argos began to laugh, but the Milesian went crimson.

"That's what I call a very unpleasant story," he said.

She began to walk slowly towards the table

2

A Princess Intervenes

IN its opening lines, the tale of King Arganthonios reads like a fairy story. His realm was very far away, beyond the Pillars of Hercules. It was a marvellously rich country; the mines produced great masses of gold and of silver; the earth was covered with fruit trees and flowers; and all his subjects were perfectly happy. That, at any rate, is what we are told. At that time, the country was called Tartessus; it is known to-day as Andalusia and is in southern Spain.

This good king would have been completely content if he had not been rather bored. The Phoenician ships used to call at his ports and the Bible tells us that they brought back most valuable cargoes. However, Arganthonios was more interested in the Greeks about whom he had heard such marvellous stories; but they never came in his direction. When they sailed towards the west, they did not like to go beyond Italy. Their ships had no decks, and were unsuited for sailing the open seas. In addition, their navigators had no maps. They could only rely on very rough descriptions of the coasts of the Mediterranean which were called *periples*. It was much easier to cruise in the Aegean Sea between small islands, scarcely ever losing sight of land, than to venture into this boundless expanse of water which extended to the west of Italy. It was believed to be a land inhabited by monsters and gods, where Ulysses—who had put in there once or twice in the past—had had to face endless dangers.

One day, when good King Arganthonios had completely given up the idea of making the Greeks appreciate his lavish hospitality, a foreign ship arrived in his principal port. It was in a sorry condition; the oars were broken and the torn sail hung in tatters.

Immediately, the boys and the women collected round the harbour.

"That ship seems to have been through a terrible storm," everyone said. "It should be put into dry dock and repaired. But where on earth can it come from?"

The captain who disembarked was a small Greek called Colaeos. To tell the truth, he had not intended to come so far or even in this direction. Having set sail from Samos, he was taking a cargo to Egypt, when he was caught by a tempest and, to his horror, he was driven by the gales to the shores of Iberia, which we know to-day as Spain.

King Arganthonios immediately sent for the Greek who, feeling he was in a friendly country, had gradually regained his confidence and ability to speak. When there is good will on both sides, people can make themselves understood even when they do not speak the same language.

The king and his guest got on so well that Arganthonios declared that he would like the Greek to remain at his court.

"Where else," said he, "will you find such a wonderful country with such wheat, such golden apples and such fine cattle?" (By "golden apples" he meant oranges.)

"That is perfectly true," answered Colaeos; "besides that, where would I find a better king? But I have a wife and children at Samos and you will understand that I cannot leave them."

So, of course, they had to part. In exchange for the cargo of cloth and pots which still remained in the battered hull of his ship, Colaeos took away a full cargo of gold and silver—enough, in fact, to make a whole town prosperous. "Heaven send," he prayed, "that the gods allow me to return safe and sound to Samos!"

Colaeos had promised Juno a valuable offering of gold and silver for her shrine, and so she protected him and he was able to glide swiftly into the port of Samos with bellying sails and a rich cargo. The goods which he brought were so valuable that he at once became the richest man in his native city. In order to make sure of his newly-gained prosperity, he took care to settle his debts with Juno. He ordered a very fine bronze jar, adorned with the heads of griffins, which was worth at least six talents. (A talent was a weight of precious metal probably roughly equal to £500 to-day.) This gift he placed on three kneeling bronze statues. Then he took the offering to the Temple of Juno. He was so pleased with his fate that he absolutely refused to return to Tartessus. "Why on earth should I run such risks, when I am so well off at home?" he thought.

Nevertheless, the story of his successful adventure was recounted everywhere along the coast of Asia Minor, in this land of Ionia where people of Greek race had been established for many years. At last it reached the ears of the inhabitants of Phocaea.

Now the countryside around the city of Phocaea did not produce enough to feed the population. But, if the Phocaeans found it hard to make a living at home, they were well equipped to find something better elsewhere. Their splendid ships were long, narrow, easy to handle and very swift, so that they were well adapted to avoid attacks from pirates and other enemies when they were at sea. These galleys were manned by fifty oarsmen, and were useful for making raids as well as for carrying cargoes.

Having heard of the great success of their compatriot, a certain number of Phocaeans set sail for the west to seek out the kingdom of Tartessus. They succeeded in their venture, and were received most hospitably by King Arganthonios who showed them the greatest friendliness. As the journey from Asia Minor was so long, the Phocaeans wished to establish a number of intermediary bases at which they could stay, take in supplies and refit. So they left Tartessus in search of other hospitable shores where they could establish colonies.

First of all, they made for Cumae—the most ancient of the Greek colonies—which was at the northern end of the Bay of Naples. From there, they sailed still further to the north and, rounding the cape which is still called after the enchantress Circe, they came ashore at the mouth of the River Tiber.

At that time, Rome was ruled by an Etruscan king called Tarquin the Elder. He was a big fat man, with very black eyes and greasy skin, like all the Etruscans. He probably showed his visitors round the little town which had a thick strong wall. At that time, small round huts and stables occupied the place where the Palace of the Caesars was to be built six hundred years later.

Tarquin probably made them understand that there could be no question of their settling in a land which he already occupied, so the Phocaeans re-embarked on their ships.

"If you sail further to the north," the Etruscan king had said, "you will find a pleasant country whose shores are inhabited by people called the Ligurians. They are neither too powerful nor too numerous, and they have plenty of land to spare."

The Phocaeans arrived at the mouth of an immense river. They had never seen anything as beautiful, for they were only accustomed to the little torrents which flow into the Aegean Sea—wretched streams that are so dried up by the month of May that there is not enough water in them to wet the beard of a goat. Naturally, they looked with the greatest respect at the swirling currents of this broad estuary where the water was divided into many channels which wound through a wilderness of pebbles and reeds. Here and there, were broad ponds where thousands of birds were swimming. Pink flamingoes stood motionless on one leg in the swamps. Far away in the distance, green hills were outlined against the sky. On seeing this wonderful land, the Greeks knelt down and placed their brows against the earth to worship the god of this mighty river. They also wished to offer a sacrifice in his honour, but they did not know how to pray to him since they had never heard his name.

At last, they caught sight of some huts of straw and wood built on piles, and some natives who shyly watched them from a distance. The explorers approached these people who were so impressed by the well-dressed new-comers and their shining weapons, that they did not attempt to run away or to fight.

"These must be Ligurians," said one of the Greeks, who was much travelled; "we must have reached their country."

And, using the few words he knew of their barbarous language, the Greek questioned the peasants who remained sullen and shy.

"They say that this river is called the Rhône, and that their king is called Nannos. He lives far from here, on the shores of a bay."

The Greeks thought that the natives might be difficult to conquer. In any case, after having explored a long stretch of the coast, they went back to Phocaea. On returning to their native city, they asked for the help of the great goddess of Ionia: Diana of Ephesus. She appeared in a dream to a woman named Aristarke. Diana told Aristarke to follow the expedition as her priestess, and to take with her a statue of the goddess.

The Phocaeans chose as their leaders a prosperous merchant called Protis and one of his friends, Simos by name.

On their return to the mouth of the River Rhône, they decided to approach King Nannos and to ask him to give them a grant of land on which to build a city. This chief lived in a hut built of rough stone, but it was considered luxurious for a Ligurian. After picking a way through the pigs and the dogs which roamed about the courtyard, the travellers noticed that furs and draperies decorated the one room of this dwelling which was otherwise so simple that there was a hole in the roof to allow the smoke from the fire to escape.

Nannos was not very much to look at, at least at first sight. Small and sallow, with grey eyes, the Ligurian chief was far from impressive. However, an intelligent observer would have noticed his strong muscles, the nimbleness of his movements, and his unusual energy. He wore a necklace of amber and green stones.

Nannos received the travellers with great courtesy and expressed his astonishment at the long journeys which they could make in their ships. Then, when they had made their request, he replied, striking the table with his fists: "My friends, we will talk business later on. To-morrow is my daughter's wedding feast. I invite you to take your place at my table with my warriors on that great occasion."

"Mighty Prince," replied Protis gently, "we accept most gratefully. We shall be happy to offer your daughter, the princess, some simple jewellery of the kind worn by the women of our country. Doubtless she is marrying some great chieftain."

"I see, my friends," replied the king, "that you do not know the customs of our country. Gyptis will choose her husband herself. She will walk round the table where my bravest warriors are seated and she will offer wine to the man of her choice."

"What a strange custom," thought the Greeks, for they were in the habit of choosing husbands for their daughters; but they took care not to make any comment.

The next day they sat at the king's table and waited

for the decisive moment with great curiosity. The future bride came in. She was small and very beautiful. Holding a cup in her hand, she stood motionless for a while; there was a deep hush throughout the room. Then she began to walk slowly towards the table and to circle round it in a leisurely manner. As she passed each guest without stopping, there was a look of astonishment and regret in the eyes of more than one young man.

Suddenly, Protis saw the cup on the table in front of him. He started up. Could this be a mistake? Or was it a courteous gesture to a stranger? Gyptis, standing by his side, remained silent, looking down at her feet. Her hands were empty.

Nannos willingly agreed to the young girl's choice. As a dowry he gave her a wide stretch of land near the sea where there was a deep and sheltered anchorage. As for Protis, he was so pleased with his good fortune that he gave thanks to the gods. On the spot where he built his city, the town of Marseilles stands to-day.

To tell the truth, the Ligurians were quite pleased with the Greeks too, for the latter taught them how to make the best of their land, how to prune vines and plant olive trees. In fact, everybody was happy as long as Nannos was alive.

When the good king died, he was succeeded by his son Comanos, who was not nearly as trustworthy as his father. He readily listened to the advice of a Ligurian who told him the following fable.

"A bitch," said he, "asked a landowner to lend her a stable for some time."

"I am going to have a litter of puppies soon," she said; "they will die of cold in this icy winter, unless you can give us a warm corner to shelter in."

"Certainly," said the good fellow. "Come in, make yourself at home."

When he returned a few days later, he saw six tiny puppies fast asleep with their noses pressed against their mother's side.

"Must I go away?" cried the bitch. "See how weak they are still. Let me stay here a little longer."

Six months later, as she was still there, the master wanted his stable back. The bitch got up, surrounded by six young mastiffs, growling and showing their teeth, and she replied: "Try to drive me out of here if you dare. The stable is mine."

Comanos understood that his friend was referring to the Greeks and thought the matter over.

A little later on, the Phocaeans were due to celebrate one of their national festivals and many of the Ligurians said they would like to be invited. The Greeks, proud of their settlement, were very much pleased and welcomed a great number of guests inside their new town. The Ligurians offered to cut wreaths, branches and flowers and brought a number of carts full of foliage within the walls.

Comanos had a brother, and this brother had a daughter. She, Comanos' neice, was in love with a Greek. In spite of the strict watch kept by her parents, she sometimes met the young man, and she longed to exchange the rough, uncultured life that she lead at home for the honourable estate of being married to a Greek. Now, on the morning of the feast, the girl came to her lover, very much troubled.

"Quickly," she whispered, "you are in the greatest danger. My uncle Comanos wants to massacre you all.

He is in hiding in the nearby creeks with his army. The carts are full of soldiers, hiding under the leaves, and each one of your guests is carrying weapons beneath his festive robes. At night, when you are all drunk, the Ligurians will rise up and murder you."

The young man rushed to Protis to tell him about the plot. All the conspirators were caught and killed. It is said that Comanos and no less than seven thousand of his warriors perished.

That is why a law was passed in the city of Marseilles ensuring that the gates would be closed on great feast days and that sentries would be stationed all along the walls.

3

The Baby in the Old Oak Chest

CORINTH to-day is a little white country town, rather dusty and slumbering, near the western extremity of the celebrated canal of that name. The channel makes a deep cut through the isthmus; from time to time, liners or merchant ships glide slowly through the water, which ripples with a sound like rustling silk, as they pass from the Ionian Sea to the Aegean. Three tall columns are all that remain of the splendours of the ancient city of Corinth, and they alone have resisted, for twenty-five centuries, the strong gusts of wind which sweep over this region. Above, rises the mountain on the topmost crest of which the Corinthians built their citadel, Acro-Corinth.

Two thousand, five hundred years ago, Corinth was a powerful city. Although the canal did not exist then, there was constant movement of merchants between the mainland of Greece and the Peloponnesus and also between the two seas. Duty had to be paid on all goods that passed, and travellers used to stay in the town. The streets of Corinth were indeed "paved with gold" and her princes lived in the greatest splendour.

At that time, there reigned over Corinth a family called the Bacchiadae who were so proud that they refused to let their daughters marry outside their family. The young Bacchiadae wed their cousins and so the crown was inherited without any kind of argument over the succession.

However, a little girl was born into this dynasty whom Nature had treated in a most unkind manner. The poor child limped, she was knock-kneed and bow-legged. She was jeered at and knicknamed Labda after the letter in the Greek alphabet shaped like her limbs. None of the cousins was prepared to marry her.

"A fine bride she would make," they remarked; "her children might be misshapen just as she is."

In order to get rid of her, the Bacchiadae made an exception to their rule and married her off to an ordinary citizen, a decent countryman, named Aetion.

The couple would have been happy in their modest way, if the gods had granted them a child; but their prayers were in vain. Labda was heartbroken and her eyes filled with tears when she saw her neighbours nursing their plump babies in the shade of the fig trees in their gardens.

"You should send your husband to consult the Oracle," people said to her. "If she promises that you will have a child, you can await its coming most joyfully; if not, you can resign yourself to the will of the gods and peace will return to you."

So Aetion set off. He crossed the isthmus and climbed

up the mountain road—worn by the feet of so many pilgrims—which leads to the sanctuary of Apollo. He went to see the Pythia.

The old prophetess did not leave him even the time to ask his question. As soon as she saw him coming she cried out: "Aetion, no one pays homage to you and yet there may well be reason to do so. You will soon receive from Labda a huge rock which will crush the tyrants who govern Corinth."

Thoroughly puzzled, Aetion returned home. Being anxious to have the prophecy explained to him, he talked about it to everyone, so much so that even the Bacchiadae heard about it. Being more cunning than the worthy fellow, these princes had no difficulty at all in interpreting the words of the Oracle: "Labda will give her husband a son who will crush the Bacchiadae."

Since they all agreed about the meaning of the prophecy, they shook their heads and looked at each other silently.

Soon the happy Labda gave birth to a son. She was absolutely delighted and the good Aetion shared fully in his wife's joy. After having looked at his new-born child, and given thanks to the gods, he went out to tell the news to his friends, and to invite them to a feast of celebration.

Someone knocked at the door. Who could these men in coarse tunics be? They wore broad belts and hobnailed boots, and their skin and their features seemed to be those of foreigners.

"What can I do for you?" asked the maidservant.

"Is your master at home?"

"He has gone out."

"We are in the service of your master; we are working at one of the timber-yards in the hills. We have brought down some wood for the temple that is being built in the square, and we should be glad to see your master's son and to congratulate the child's mother."

The maidservant took them in to see her mistress. The newborn child was there, sleeping in his wickerwork cradle. Labda was quite surprised for she did not know these men, but she felt that she could not send them away since they came with smiling faces, blessing the gods, to congratulate her.

"That is a fine boy," they said.

Labda was quite ready to agree with them.

"How heavy he must be!"

She certainly agreed with them on that point, and so she could scarcely stop them from picking him up.

The oldest among them, who seemed to be their spokesman, stooped down and picked the child out of its cradle. He pressed him in his great hairy hands.

"Gently, my friends," cried the mother.

Gently? But why should this tall stranger be gentle? What is he going to do with this child, at whom he looks in a searching and almost wicked way?

Then something strange happened. His eyes flickered; their stern gaze grew suddenly gentler. The tiny, weak child had awakened. The man and the child looked at each other for a while and suddenly the little face relaxed and broke into a fascinating smile, a smile full of trust, tenderness and delight. He waved his little pink hands about as if he expected to be caressed.

The bearded giant turned, wiping away the drops of sweat which formed suddenly on his forehead. He opened his mouth to speak, then shut it again. He held out the baby to one of his companions and said in a low voice: "Take him, I cannot do it."

The other man shrugged his shoulders and seized the child, who lay in his arms, pink and full of joyous laughter.

"And I can't either," murmured the man. "Here, you!" He moved towards a third who promptly placed the child in its cradle. The soldiers—for soldiers they were—turned about and went away.

Labda was pale and her heart was beating. "What a strange visit," she thought. What were they talking about? What had they meant to do to her child? Had they really gone? She tiptoed noiselessly as far as the door and looked out at them through a peephole. They had not gone away. They were outside, discussing something. She listened, and what she heard chilled her with fear. They were quarrelling and accusing each other.

"You are nothing but a coward," said one.

"And you, are you any better?" answered the other.

"And what will the king say? He will have us all flogged to death if we don't bring him back the body of this child."

Labda had heard quite enough. She rushed up to her son; whilst the murderers were knocking loudly at her door, she quietly put the baby into a corn bin, closed down the lid and prepared to face the danger.

In vain they broke in the door, stormed and searched. Labda did not speak; she remained motionless, offering up a prayer to all the gods.

"As long as my child does not cry, as long as they don't open the corn bin," she thought.

Each time the murderers came near to the hiding-place where she had put her treasure, her heart stopped beating and she murmured to herself, "Ye gods!"

But the gods took pity on her; now she heard the voice of Aetion in the courtyard. He was coming back accompanied by his good friends and neighbours. In a twinkling of an eye the intruders vanished. The child was saved!

In memory of the coffer which preserved his life, the coffer which the Greeks call *kupsas*, the child was nicknamed Kupselos.

When he grew up, he fulfilled the prophecy of the Oracle and drove out the Bacchiadae who had tried to kill him.

4

A Very Strange City

 RIVER, called the Eurotas and lined with bulrushes, flows across a small plain in the heart of the Peloponnesus. It is surrounded by mountains and, in winter, the snow covers the peaks of the Taygetus range. It is the plain of Laconia. The traveller who visits this region to-day will find no monuments there at all, not a temple column, not a tier of an amphitheatre, not even a half-buried statue, to indicate that here once stood a mighty city. However it is the site of one of the most notable towns in Greece, the great rival of Athens, the redoubtable Sparta, also called Lacedaemon.

Have you ever heard anyone say of a courageous young man who gives up every pleasure to devote himself to duty: "He is a real 'Spartan'!" Have you heard of a "Spartan education"? If anybody speaks tersely, we accuse him of being "laconic". These are references to the customs of the Spartans.

It is thought that Sparta owed much of her glory and her power to these customs. The least that we can say is that they aroused the curiosity of the Greeks so that numerous writers described what happened in Sparta, and that all sorts of moving and amusing stories were told about its inhabitants.

It is said that, in the dim remoteness of time, Sparta was governed by kings who claimed to be descended from the hero Hercules (whom the Greeks called Heracles), but these princes had become very degenerate. They ruled their subjects badly with the result that there were constant disorders. People fought in the streets and, in trying to separate two citizens who were quarrelling, King Eunomas was stabbed to death.

He left two sons, Polydectus and Lycurgus. Polydectus, the elder, succeeded his father. But by ill-chance, he died soon after, leaving his wife and a newborn baby to mourn him. The widow of Polydectus, a really wicked woman, suggested to Lycurgus that she would get rid of the child, on condition that he married her and thus became king. Lycurgus refused to do this. Instead, he entrusted the child to reliable people and, fearing that if his nephew died he would be accused of his death, he decided to set off on a long journey.

He visited Crete, Asia Minor and Egypt; some people even affirm that he went as far as India. In every country he studied the form of government, the laws and the customs, and consulted the elders and the wise men so that he could assess which were the best methods of ruling nations.

The Spartans, discontented with the confusion which prevailed in their city, begged him to return and offered him complete freedom to reform its laws. After having sacrificed to the gods, he went to Delphi to obtain the sanction of Apollo for what he was about to do. Then Lycurgus drew up the laws which bear his name, and ensured the glory of Sparta, giving it a character that is remembered even in the present day.

Lycurgus placed all the land under common ownership, including the meadows and the fallow land, the stony soil, the marshes, the forests and the fine fields which bear the best harvests in summer. He shared out these lands in equal parts and gave some to each citizen; but these citizens were not allowed to cultivate the land themselves, for the Helots—a race whom the Spartans had reduced to eternal slavery—did this work. The real citizen of Sparta was only interested in war or in ruling the country.

Thus, the Spartans only thought of living like soldiers, of preparing for war or waging it, of conquering territories, or even quite simply of gaining glory.

In the rest of Greece, people jeered at the way they lived, at their harsh life and austere ways. There were no craftsmen, lacemakers or jewellers in Sparta, for they would have found no customers for their work. Clad in the coarsest woollen cloth, the men spent the whole day together. They ate, in groups of twenty, a simple meal of which the main dish was the famous black gruel. This was a kind of porridge which the Spartans liked better than anything else, and even old men would exchange their share of meat for a bowl of this gruel. It is only fair to say that this taste was not shared by everybody. It is said that Denys, the rich Tyrant of Syracuse, about whom the Greeks told so many stories, was anxious to try this gruel one day. He bought a Spartan slave and made him prepare a dish of gruel with the greatest possible care. No sooner had Denys put a spoonful of it in his mouth, than he spat it out again.

"Ough!" cried he, "how on earth can the Spartans like anything so disgusting?"

"To appreciate it properly, my lord," replied the cook, "you must first of all take exercise in the Spartan way, and go swimming in the ice-cold water of the Eurotas."

The perfect Spartan was, before everything else, a perfect soldier. Lycurgus had so much confidence in the courage of his fellow-citizens that he would not even allow ramparts to be built round the town.

"Here are the walls of Sparta," said one of the kings, pointing to his soldiers.

When another was asked how far the kingdom of Sparta extended, he replied: "As far as this javelin will carry," and threw the weapon which he held in his hand with all his might.

The Spartan troops marched to combat to the music of flutes and it is said that one of the most moving spectacles imaginable was to see a company of these proud warriors setting out to war; they sang joyously as they rushed forward to their death. The king always marched at the head of his men and it was a great honour to be allowed to walk by his side. This privilege was often reserved for an athlete who had been victorious in the Games.

One day, during the Olympic Games, a competitor offered a Spartan gymnast a huge sum of money to withdraw from the contest which he was likely to win. The Spartan refused this proposition, fought and triumphed;

instead of the money this dishonest transaction would have brought, he received the simple laurel wreath awarded to victors.

After the proclamation of the results, he was accosted by his rival who said to him scornfully: "You would have done better to accept my proposition, for by now you would be rich. What has your victory brought you? Just a wreath of leaves!"

"Does the honour of walking by the side of your king mean nothing to you?" replied the athlete nobly.

It is always a disgrace for a soldier to run away but, for a Spartan, it was a lasting dishonour. This is the explanation of the story of the three hundred Spartans, commanded by Leonidas, who faced inevitable death without flinching.

One day, a stranger met a lame Spartan soldier who was setting out to war.

"Now my friend," he asked him, "what use are you in the army? You should ask for a horse."

"What could I do with it?" replied the cripple. "Do we need men who move fast? If I stand firm at my post that is all that is required of me."

"How did you become so famous?" another man was asked.

"By despising death."

Talkativeness was not encouraged in Laconia. Lycurgus really despised all forms of oratory. "If you are in the right," he would say, "there is no need to say much, but if you are in the wrong, it is better to hold your tongue."

All the same, people mocked the Spartans for their

brevity and, even to-day, we say that a man of few words is laconic. Spartan children learnt at an early age to be silent; it was only when they grew up that they were allowed to speak in public and then they were asked to use as few words as possible.

Needless to say, the Spartans thoroughly despised people who lied or betrayed their trust, and they even hesitated to make use of them. A deserter once offered to lead some Spartan soldiers into a citadel which was held by his own countrymen. When a young officer was told to pick a hundred of his best men to follow the enemy traitor, he replied: "Is it reasonable, my lords, to entrust the safety of our brave soldiers to a scoundrel who betrays his own country?"

From the day of their birth, Spartan children were brought up in a very curious manner. As soon as they were born they were washed in wine. Spartan nurses declared that weakly children did not survive baths of this kind, and they thought that that was all to the good. Spartan babies were not wrapped up at all, so that they could wave their limbs about as much as they liked. That was, of course, very healthy and very pleasant for them, but if they started crying, they found no sympathy. There was no question of snivelling if they did not like their gruel or if they were afraid of the dark.

At seven years old, little boys had to leave their mother and live with boys of the same age. They were under the control of young men and had to learn to obey before commanding. When they could spell simple words, it was thought that they were educated, but they were never considered to have had enough training in the handling of arms, in riding, walking long distances and swimming. Barefooted, with shaven heads, wearing only a skimpy cloak in winter and stark naked in summer, they carried out any order without flinching. At night, they slept on reeds gathered from the banks of the Eurotas with their bare hands; they were not even allowed to use a knife to cut them. The thinner they were the swifter and the surer were their movements—it was thought—and so their food was scanty and unpalatable.

Some of the Spartan customs may appear absurd, but others were admirable. Nowhere were old people so much honoured as in Sparta. It was considered infamous to remain seated in the presence of an older man. When it was suggested to one young wounded Spartan that he should be carried on a stretcher, he replied: "Never! I should not be able to stand up if an old man happened to pass."

Such were the laws and customs introduced by Lycurgus. It would be easy to imagine from this that he was a very severe person. On the contrary, he was very cheerful and sometimes really witty. He decreed that a statue of the God of Laughter should be placed in all dining-rooms; that was surely a good idea.

When he had finished his reforms, Lycurgus assembled all the citizens of Sparta and exhorted them to observe his laws and customs very faithfully.

"They are harsh," he said to them, "but they will make you virtuous, and if you remain virtuous, you will be happy. Swear to respect them, at any rate, until my return."

They all took this oath and Lycurgus departed.

He went to Delphi, and asked the Oracle if the laws were good.

"Perfect," replied Apollo, "so long as Sparta observes them she will surpass all other cities in glory."

Lycurgus wrote down this pronouncement and sent it to Sparta. Then he embraced his friends and his son, told them to leave him, for he had made up his mind to die so that his compatriots should remain bound by their oath forever.

He refused to eat and died in the prime of life. His bones were brought back to Sparta, and it is said that his tomb was struck by a thunderbolt as a sign that the gods claimed this hallowed place for themselves.

5

The Most Unusual Women in Greece

URIOUS is certainly the right word to describe the life of the Spartans. They needed mothers and wives of their own type, so there are just as many amusing stories told about the women as about the men. At that time, in the rest of Greece, well-bred women lived in complete seclusion and prided themselves on their modesty.

Cut off from the outside world, in a separate part of the house called the *gynaeceum*, they spent most of their time at home; they span and they wove; they did the housekeeping and they scarcely ever went out unless they were accompanied by a maidservant. Their long robes and their delicate sandals prevented them from taking any exercise. Dignity and discretion were their ideal virtues; they did not appear at meetings and feasts for men, and were seen as little as possible in public places.

However, Lycurgus came to the conclusion that, in order to breed strong men and to bring them up to face hardship, women of the same type were required, women whose bodies and spirit were toughened by sports of all kinds and who were brought up like men. It is possible that he was right.

The young girls of Sparta wore short dresses held in by a girdle. The Greeks of other regions used to jeer at their bare legs, but these girls could use a bow or throw a javelin as well as any man, and they could swim, run and throw the discus with the same ease as boys of their own age.

Artemis (Diana)—the huntress so often represented, bow in hand and wearing the short Spartan tunic—was their goddess. From time to time, they would assemble opposite boys of their age and make fun of them in their songs. The fine, courageous athletes attracted these girls; but the cowards, the idlers and those unskilled in sports or games were jeered at by them and by the onlookers. Later on, when they got married, these Spartan women exercised a great deal of influence on their husbands.

One foreign woman said rather enviously to the wife of the great general, Leonidas: "You Spartan women seem to dominate your men."

The soldier's wife replied: "But why not? We women bring men into the world!"

The Spartan women brought up their children in the way that they themselves had been trained; their motherly love did not prevent them having a stern sense of duty.

When one mother learnt that her son had deserted and taken refuge in a foreign land, she wrote to him as follows: "My son, there is a most unpleasant rumour about you. You must either refute it or kill yourself."

Another mother was waiting at the gates of a town for news about a battle in which her six sons had fought. A messenger appeared. She rushed forward but before she could say a word, the soldier cried out: "Poor woman your five sons are dead."

"That is not what I asked you, you scoundrel," she replied. "How did the battle go?"

"We were victorious."

"Well," she said, "I am quite satisfied and can put up with the loss of my children."

6

Croesus: Happiest of Men

ONG ago, in the year 506 B.C., a man named Croesus became king of Lydia at the age of thirty-five. The Lydians lived in Asia Minor, and Sardis was their capital. Pactolus, the principal river of the region, was noted for the gold in its sands which was a great source of prosperity. The Greeks knew this country well, for their colonies in Asia Minor did a great deal of trade with the Lydians.

The new king's first care was to erect a most extraordinary tomb for his father. It was visited for many centuries afterwards, as it was considered to be one of the marvels of the Ancient World. The base was built of enormous stones, but the rest of the monument consisted of piled-up earth; people of every class brought their share of earth to help in the construction.

Then Croesus interested himself in the administration of his kingdom and proved to be a great king. He conquered many of the neighbouring countries and brought back so much gold to Sardis that his wealth became proverbial. In those days, just as in the present time, people talked of being "as rich as Croesus".

Travellers came from all parts of the world to visit his capital, and Croesus encouraged them to do so, for he loved fame. One day an Athenian named Solon was presented to him. He was a very wise man and also very famous, though not at all in the same way as Croesus. His fellow-citizens trusted him so much that they had asked him to make them a new set of laws. After having accomplished this difficult task in Athens, Solon travelled a little in order to get new ideas.

Croesus had not the slightest doubt that this man, who came from a country where the goats have more thorns to eat than clover, would be dazzled at the sight of his treasures. "Show him everything," he ordered.

Obliging guides showed the visitor round every corner of the palace. They pointed out the carpets, the purple hangings, the enormous basins made of precious metals, the statues of ivory and gold, and the vases made of the finest marble. They opened up the strong-rooms for him and made him look at the jewelled swords, the ingots of gold and the strings of pearls. Solon, who was not given to talking, did not say a word. Rather disappointed, the guides brought the stranger back to the king.

"Well, my friend," cried Croesus; "are you satisfied? I have heard your wisdom praised, and doubtless your journeys have given you great experience of life. Tell me, of all the men that you have seen, who is the happiest?"

Solon bowed politely and replied: "Your majesty, it is Tellus of Athens."

"How can that be?" asked Croesus, very much surprised, for this was not the answer he had expected.

Solon explained: "Tellus was a citizen of a prosperous city. Isn't that a great source of happiness? His children and his grandchildren were handsome and good. He was reasonably wealthy. Then he died in a most enviable manner: he fought for his country and behaved with such courage that he ensured victory for his side and met the most glorious death on the field of battle. The Athenians buried him with every kind of honour in the place where he had died."

"Very well," said Croesus, "and after him?"

"Cleobis and Biton, noble king. They belonged to an excellent family in Argos. They also had reasonable wealth, but their physical strength was quite exceptional, so that they were frequently victorious in the Games. They met their death in an astonishing manner. It was at the time when the people of Argos used to celebrate the feast of Juno, their divine protectress, with unsurpassed brilliance.

"The mother of these young men was so ill that she could only go to the temple by chariot. She waited for a long time for the oxen which had been sent for. Time passed and the ox-team did not arrive. So these splendid sons put the yoke over their shoulders and dragged their venerable mother in a cart to the temple. They proceeded like this for about five miles and arrived still in harness at Argos. The crowd congratulated the proud mother with enthusiasm. She, full of love for her wonderful sons, went into the sanctuary and, standing before Juno—the protectress of Argos, queen of mothers and of wives—she raised up her hands to heaven and cried: 'Grant O mighty goddess, that the greatest good fortune be given to my sons Cleobis and Biton.'

"The celebrations continued and the young men took part in the sacrifice and then in the feast; at last towards evening, they fell asleep in the sanctuary and no one could wake them up. They were dead.

"You can see their statues, O great king. They are at Delphi where the people of Argos have set them up to the memory of these exceptional men."

This time, Croesus could not restrain his anger.

"And so that is what you think, my friend," he cried. "And what about the happiness of the king who speaks to you now? Am I less than Tellus, less than two private citizens of Argos?"

"Croesus," replied Solon, "do not forget the gods. They are jealous and capable of doing great harm. You have now reached the height of prosperity I agree, and I can assure you that I am delighted about it. Until he is dead, let us not say that a man is happy, but rather that he is favoured by fortune."

Solon was speaking to the most prosperous of the princes of Asia, but he did not succeed in convincing him, still less in satisfying him. Croesus bade him a cold farewell and did not give the Greek the rich gifts prepared for him.

But this is not the end of the story.

7

You Cannot Escape Your Fate

 ARIOUS writers have declared that Croesus was not the happiest of men, for one of his two sons was deaf and dumb. Worse still, there was a terrifying prediction that if Croesus tried to cure the young man, the day on which he spoke would be one of great misfortune. So Croesus used to ignore the poor handicapped lad and behaved as if the gods had given him only one son, Atys. The latter was handsome, pleasant, highly intelligent and a first-class athlete. He surpassed the young men of his own age in his accomplishments as much as his father surpassed other kings of his time in wealth.

One night, Croesus had a dream in which he saw Atys die after having been struck by a sharp-pointed piece of iron. Still bathed in sweat and trembling in all his limbs, he sent for his marshal and ordered him to remove from the palace every weapon, arrow, javelin and pointed

The exhausted animal crouched on its haunches

sword. He then forbade the use of such implements for fear that one of them should wound the prince. Moreover, he prevented his son from joining the army. This was a great grievance to the young man who would normally have been in command of the troops.

One day a young fugitive came to Sardis. He went to the palace of Croesus and beseeched the king to purify him as he was guilty of a murder. In those days, a criminal was considered to be accursed by the gods. Even if he fled and thus protected himself from the penalties of the law, he was still believed to be impure and a bearer of misfortune. Nevertheless, certain priests and princes who looked on themselves as demi-gods could remove the curse by special ceremonies. This Croesus did.

Then he questioned the fugitive: "You don't look like a scoundrel. Will you tell me your name?"

"I am a Phrygian," replied the young man, "and of royal blood. My name is Adrastus. Alas! I killed my brother by accident, but my father drove me away and I am an outlaw and have lost everything."

"I knew your father, Adrastus, and I loved him dearly. You may stay with me, as a friend and an honoured guest."

Shortly afterwards, an immense wild boar came down from the mountains of Mysia and spread panic everywhere. Its enormous tusks rooted up the ground and destroyed trees. It trampled down the crops and even— it was said with terror—devoured babies in their cradles and the little shepherds in the fields. The Mysians, who were neighbours and subjects of the king of Lydia, sent an embassy to their lord and master.

"Send us the best huntsmen of your kingdom," they

implored, "under the leadership of your son, who is so skilled in tracking down and killing wild beasts."

"As for my son," said Croesus, "don't even suggest it; but I will willingly send you my best huntsmen."

At this point, the young prince came into the audience room and immediately understood what they were discussing.

"Father," said he, "I am covered with shame. I used to be the most courageous of your warriors and the most expert at the chase. Now you have not only kept me out of the army, but you will not even allow me the honour of leading the proudest young men of this country to track down this monster. To please you, I have just taken a wife. What will she think of me?"

So Croesus explained the fatal secret to the young man.

"Is that all, Father?" cried Atys joyously. "Don't you see that there is no risk? In your dream, I died of an iron shaft. That cannot apply to a wild boar, since his tusks are of ivory. You must agree to that, Father. Please let me go!"

Only half-convinced, Croesus gave way. Then he sent for Adrastus.

"Young Phrygian," he said, "you owe me everything. I have not sent for you to reproach you, but to ask you to watch most carefully over my son. Go, accompany him on this hunt and bring him back safe and sound."

"Oh, king and benefactor," replied the young man, "you can rely on me."

They set off. Never did such courageous and well-armed young men attack a more dangerous quarry. As soon as they had reached the coverts, hounds were unleashed and they rushed after the wild beast. It was one of the biggest boars ever heard of and often turned on the hounds which pursued it. At last, the beast was forced into the densest of thickets.

Now the exhausted animal crouched on its haunches as the hounds came up like a rising tide. Transfixed and thrown up into the air by the tusks, the boldest hounds fell back covered with blood. Then, seeing the boar at bay, the huntsmen surrounded it. Excited by the ardour of the chase, brandishing their weapons, they pressed forward, laughing and jostling each other, their eyes fixed on the lone monster which was now hemmed in by the hounds.

"He is yours, Atys!"

"Take him, Adrastus."

The Phrygian threw his javelin and it whistled through the air. Alas! It struck the young prince through the heart. Bathed in his own blood, he collapsed, turned pale and died.

What a tragic return! What a funeral procession! The unfortunate Adrastus, walking next to the dead body of Atys, prayed for death. What a sad moment it was when Croesus rushed towards the prostrate body of his son.

"Prince," said Adrastus in a broken voice. "See in what state I bring back your son. Take pity on me, noble king, kill me over his dead body."

But Croesus shook his head.

"The guilt belongs to the gods alone. Years ago a soothsayer warned me of this. As for you, unfortunate youth, you are not responsible in any way."

This generosity was too much for Adrastus; it completely overwhelmed him. The funeral ceremony began. The young prince's body was burnt on a pyre of cedar wood surrounded by the most sumptuous offerings. Then his ashes were buried. Around his tomb there was a great silence. Speechless with sorrow, all those who had loved him bade him farewell in their hearts. All this was more than Adrastus could bear; he took a few steps forward, approached the mound of fresh earth and stabbed himself to the heart.

8

A King who was Suspicious of Oracles

AFTER the death of his well-beloved son, Croesus spent two years in the deepest retirement, for he was overwhelmed by sorrow. However, affairs of state claimed his attention and so, in spite of everything, he was kept busy. His neighbours, the Persians, were beginning to cause him anxiety. For centuries past the Persians and their kinsmen the Medes lived on the plain of Iran. (To-day, there is still a state called Iran or Persia.)

For the past few years, these people had been expanding their territory at the expense of their neighbours. Under their young king, Cyrus, the Persians swiftly conquered all the nearby lands and built up a huge empire. Cyrus became so powerful that Croesus grew anxious and wondered whether he would not do well to declare war on him before he grew even stronger.

Whilst he was still hesitating, he went to consult the Oracles of the gods. Usually, kings and princes first called upon the Pythia of Delphi.

Croesus sought out all the Oracles in order to test them and choose the best. Alas! The gods do not like people to doubt them, so they plotted together to lead Croesus astray.

He sent messengers to all the Oracles of world fame: Delphi, Dodona with its talking oak trees and Ammon, the horned god of Lybia in North Africa. Neither did he forget the less celebrated Oracles such as Trophonius in his cave, the hero Amphiaraus and the Branchidae priests at Miletus. To all his messengers he gave the same orders.

"You will allow ninety-nine days to pass from the date of your departure and, on the hundredth, you will ask the oracle what King Croesus is doing at that precise moment. Then you will return swiftly and bring me back the reply."

The Pythia was not at all disconcerted. She gave the king's messengers a reply in verse, which was remarkably simple:

"I can count the grains of the sand on the shore and the drops of water in the sea.

"I can make the deaf to hear, and hear the speech of the dumb.

"Cooked with the flesh of a newborn lamb is the flesh of the turtle, in a bronze receptacle, and the savour of the cooking comes to my nostrils.

"Bronze is in the earth beneath her and with bronze she is covered."

Croesus was astonished by this; on the hundredth day after the departure of his messengers he had been busy boiling together a turtle and a lamb in a bronze cauldron with a bronze lid. It was not the sort of thing that he did usually but he had thought out this extraordinary occupation in order to test the Oracle. Besides, the Pythia was not the only one to reply in this vein. The Oracle of Amphiaraus did his best, and Croesus found his reply admirable too.

King Croesus then decided that he would ask the most important question at Delphi and from Amphiaraus. He thought that most probably gods were like men and gave most satisfaction to their customers if paid in advance and paid very well indeed. So he sent to Delphi a vast quantity of rich offerings: three thousand head of cattle, beds covered with sheets of gold, cups of solid gold, garments of the finest linen dyed purple, a hundred bars of solid gold, two great silver and gold basins in which to mix water and wine, forty barrels of silver, the golden statue of a woman (it is said that it was the portrait of his baker's wife), his wife's jewels and, last of all, a lion in solid gold. For many years this lion was greatly admired by visitors to Delphi. Alas, then there was a fire, and it melted like butter and lost half its weight. What was left was still very valuable, so it was placed in the treasury of the Spartans.

The king did not forget the hero Amphiaraus either; he sent him a shield and a spear—in gold, of course!

The king's messengers then questioned the two Oracles to find out if he should take up arms against the Persians.

You can imagine how pleased Croesus was when both Oracles gave him precisely the same reply, which seemed as clear as crystal: "If he takes up arms," they prophe-sied, "he will destroy a great empire."

Overwhelmed with gratitude, Croesus immediately sent two pieces of gold to each of the inhabitants of Delphi. Delighted by this generous gift, the Elders of the city declared that henceforth the king would have priority whenever he wished to consult the Pythia, and that every Lydian should have the same rights as their own citizens.

Wishing to take every precaution, and presuming on the immense gifts that he had made, the king decided to consult Apollo—the resident god of Delphi—for a third time. "Will my Empire last long?" he asked.

"When a mule shall become king of the Medes, you may without shame take flight along the banks of the River Hermus, O Lydian," replied the god through the mouth of his priestess.

The king thought this an excellent joke; he considered it a subtle way of predicting that his rule would last for ever.

He began to prepare for war without delay.

9

Solon! Solon! Solon!

THOUGH he had already begun his preparations for war, Croesus had a last opportunity to save himself, for one of his subjects said to him: "O, great king! Why should you wish to attack the Persians? They are so poor that they have to wear the skins of animals; they drink only water and theirs is a barren land. If you are the victor, you gain nothing and if you are beaten . . ."

Croesus merely shrugged his shoulders. Soon afterwards he led the whole of his army towards the River Halys, the frontier between Lydia and the kingdom of Persia. It is said that he crossed this river thanks to the skill and intelligence of a Greek engineer named Thales who came from one of the Greek colonies in Asia Minor with whom the Lydians, and later on the Persians, were in constant contact.

There were no bridges, and Croesus did not know what to do, but Thales offered to divert half the river behind the army. The other half of the river would then be easy to ford.

When this was done, the Lydian army boldly advanced into enemy territory and soon clashed with Cyrus' Persian army. The very fierce battle remained indecisive but, when night fell, the Lydians were forced to withdraw.

After this semi-defeat, Croesus fell back on Sardis. Here, he hoped to regroup his armies, receive reinforcements from his allies and spend the winter under shelter. Scarcely had he entered his capital when the whole surrounding district became infested by snakes. Stranger still, the horses left the pastures, attacked the snakes and ate them up. The seers shook their heads and looked glum.

"It's a bad omen," they said. "The snakes, children of the Lydian soil, have been annihilated by the horses, warlike animals from foreign lands."

Now Cyrus, the Persian, was a skilful general and did not give his enemy time to recover. He appeared before Sardis at the precise moment when the unfortunate Croesus believed that he was absolutely safe. Now the two armies fought beneath the walls of the capital. The Lydians were fine horsemen and their cavalry-men were dangerous since they were armed with long, sharp javelins. When Cyrus saw them lined up in battle order he began to feel anxious.

"O, King of Kings," said one of his officers to him, "you have no reason to be afraid. Have you forgotten how much horses hate the smell of camels? Since we have so many of them for our transport, order them to be placed in the front line opposite the Lydian cavalry."

This manœuvre succeeded beyond their wildest hopes.

The Lydian horses bolted and, in spite of the courage of their riders who dismounted and fought on foot, the carnage was frightful. Soon the Lydians were forced to take refuge behind the walls of their capital where they were besieged by the Persians.

Sardis was a very strong fortress; in fact, one side of the city was considered to be absolutely inaccessible, so impenetrable that the ancestor of the Lydian king, the legendary Meles, had refused to take normal precautions in this sector. Indeed, a young lion had been born in the palace, and the seers had declared that the town wall would be impenetrable wherever the animal was led. Meles had not even troubled to have it taken on this side where there was a sheer drop.

The siege had already lasted twelve days; the inhabitants of the city had put up a stout resistance. On the thirteenth day, towards evening, a Lydian, who was leaning on the part of the parapet which overlooked the precipice, allowed his helmet to fall and it rolled down to the bottom. Without hesitation, he let himself down the wall, worked his way to the bottom, picked up the helmet, and went back to his post.

Unknown to the Lydian, a Persian named Hyriad had seen this exploit and it made him think.

On the next day, the fourteenth day of the siege, some horsemen of the Royal Guard, galloped round the different units of the Persian army. "Great will be the reward to the first soldier who reaches the top of the ramparts," they shouted. Hyriad made up his mind to try to win the prize.

When he started to climb he found the ascent much easier than he had thought, so he called out to his comrades and, in the twinkling of an eye, hundreds of Persians were over the ramparts. Taking the garrison from behind, they captured Sardis.

Croesus fought like a madman, and his last son, the deaf and dumb boy, kept by his side. Suddenly, a Persian approached from behind and raised his javelin to throw it at the king. The unfortunate youth, torn from his silence by terror and grief cried: "Man, don't kill Croesus!"

From that moment, he recovered the use of his speech and so the prediction about him came true.

In any case, Croesus was captured, loaded with chains and taken before Cyrus who condemned him to be burnt alive, together with fourteen young Lydian nobles—fourteen was the number of years that Croesus had reigned. The unfortunate king was the first to climb onto the pyre. There, remembering his past prosperity and the greatness of his fall, Croesus began to moan in a loud voice, "Solon! Solon! Solon!"

"What does he say?" asked Cyrus, who had not taken his eyes off him. "Send him my interpreters."

So they questioned Croesus, but the king shook his head without replying.

On being further pressed, he cried out at last: "Solon was a man whose advice would be more profitable to kings than the greatest wealth."

When the interpreters tried to find out more, Croesus refused to explain.

"Leave me alone! Leave me alone!" he cried. "Haven't you tormented me enough?"

At last, he agreed to tell the story and, as he talked, the interpreters translated everything to Cyrus. Now the executioners, not in the least interested in what they heard, had just set fire to the faggots. Already black wreaths of smoke were beginning to rise, already the flames were spreading quickly over the dry wood with a crackling noise: the end of Croesus was nigh.

However, Cyrus was moved by the sad tale of his former enemy and forgot his anger.

"Put out the fire," he cried.

Alas, it was impossible to obey. However much they tried, fresh flames sprang up. In vain, the soldiers ran to draw water; in vain, the executioners removed the faggots out of reach of the flames. The pitiless furnace grew ever fiercer and already the fire was beginning to touch the feet of the wretched victim, when Croesus raised beseeching hands towards heaven.

"Apollo, God of Delphi," he cried through his tears. "Lord of the Oracles, remember the past! If ever my offerings found pleasure in your eyes, if I lavished gold on you and made endless sacrifices in your honour, save me in this moment of great peril."

When he began to speak, the sky was still a clear blue, but suddenly a dense black cloud appeared overhead, there was a roar of thunder and a deluge of rain drenched the burning furnace which soon became no more than a pile of steaming charcoal.

Croesus, set free from the stake, was brought before his conqueror. Cyrus made him sit by his side, treated him with the greatest courtesy, and took off the chains himself.

As the unhappy king appeared to be overwhelmed and pensive, Cyrus said to him with great kindness: "O Croesus, have you any request to make of me?"

"By all means, O my master and conqueror," replied the defeated monarch. "See these chains from which you have just freed me, if you will kindly allow me to do so, I would like to send them to Delphi, to this god whom I greatly respect."

Cyrus heard how his rival had consulted the different Oracles, and he readily agreed to this request.

So an embassy of Lydians set out for Delphi and hung the chains of Croesus outside the gates of the temple.

"Why did you deceive Croesus, O God of Delphi," they asked. "Why these lying prophecies? Your temple still overflows with his offerings. Is it the custom for the Greek gods to be ungrateful?"

The Pythia immediately explained herself.

"Did I not tell you," she cried, "that your king would destroy a great empire? Well, which empire was referred to? Cyrus' or his? Should he not have asked me this question before anything else? And, if he had had a trace of wisdom, would he not have interpreted my second reply: 'When a mule will be king of the Medes.' Well, what is a mule? The offspring of an ass and of a mare, the mingling of two different races. Who is Cyrus? The son of a Median princess and of a Persian of obscure birth. That is what you must tell Croesus. As for the gratitude of Apollo, Croesus is the last who should speak of it, since it is thanks to the god that he has been saved from a most desperate situation."

The messengers reported these explanations to Croesus and, since he had to admit that they were sound, he bowed his head and his heart was filled with humility. "I alone am to blame," he sighed.

In fact, the fate of Croesus was not nearly so harsh as

he might have feared. Cyrus kept him by his side as a friend and even as a counsellor, for he was struck by the moderation and excellence of the advice given by Croesus, due to real but belated wisdom.

PART TWO

STORIES OF POLYCRATES, PISISTRATUS, THE MEDES AND THE PERSIANS

10

The Danger of being too Happy

PLACE the map of the Mediterranean in front of you, then run your finger along the coast of Asia Minor from north to south. You will soon come upon the town of Miletus. Miletus is one of the colonies which Greeks from Europe founded on the edge of the Asiatic continent long ago. Opposite Miletus you will find the island of Samos, noted for its wines, but very poor to-day, though it had many years of prosperity in the past.

In about the year 532 B.C. civil war broke out in Samos and the man who had caused this trouble achieved absolute power and maintained it by force of arms. The Greeks called men of this type tyrants. Among the more distinguished tyrants were: Pisistratus in Athens, Cypselus in Corinth, Phidon in Argos, later Gelon in Syracuse, and later still, the celebrated Denys the Ancient.

So Polycrates became tyrant of Samos. At first he shared the island with his brothers, but he killed the

elder, and drove away the younger one, keeping everything for himself. Then he built huge galleys, each manned by fifty oars, and took a thousand archers into his
service so that he could plunder the islands and the mainland.

When he was reproached for ravaging and robbing
friends and foes alike, he replied: "Why should I make
any exceptions? If I give back to my friends what I have
taken away from them, see how pleased they will be; and
much happier than if I had not taken anything away
from them."

It was then that, unable to endure the vile behaviour
of this brigand any longer, the wise Pythagoras left
Samos. First of all he travelled for some time in order to
gain experience and knowledge, then he settled at Crotona where he established his celebrated school.

Polycrates did not appear to resent the departure of
Pythagoras. He hardly noticed it, in fact, for everything
that he did succeeded, and money, treasures and prisoners
were brought back by his ships in vast quantities.

Very much impressed by these activities, Amasis king
of Egypt became his ally. Polycrates was so lucky that
Amasis grew anxious. The people of the Ancient World
were always ready to believe that the gods became jealous
of those who were too fortunate, and, of course, the
jealousy of the gods always ended by bringing some cata-
strophe. So Amasis wrote the following letter:

*My dear Polycrates, I am sure that the gods are becoming
jealous, for everyone on whom fortune has lavished its gifts too
generously comes to a bad end. You should, therefore, take
some precautions. Choose the thing that you like best and*

*destroy it. If, after this sacrifice, you still have the misfortune
to be lucky, resign yourself to a new sacrifice, and to a third
one if things continue in this way.*

Polycrates really appreciated this advice. He reflected
carefully, asking himself what he liked best in the world.
He owned a wonderful gold seal engraved with exquisite
skill by a noted artist, and now he decided that, of all his
possessions, there was nothing he liked better.

So he put out to sea in one of his great galleys and,
when he was far from land, he took out the jewel and
threw it into the depths of the waters, sighing heavily as
he did so. Then he ordered the crew to row swiftly back
to harbour. His heart was full of sadness, but his mind
was at rest.

Five or six days later a fisherman of Samos caught a
fish of great size in his nets. It was so fine that he presented it to the tyrant in the hopes of being given a large
reward.

"O king," he said, "I am very poor and I live by my
work, but this catch seemed to me to be worthy of you
alone. Allow me to present it to you."

Highly pleased, Polycrates had the fish taken to his
kitchen and invited the fisherman to dinner. It was
cooked with an exquisite sauce and placed on the table
in a silver dish. When it was carved up, everyone was surprised. In its stomach lay the emerald and gold seal. Joyously, the servants handed it to their master who received it with the greatest astonishment.

On hearing of this miracle, Amasis immediately sent a
herald to denounce his alliance with this tyrant who was
too lucky. This second letter ran:

> *I cannot bear to remain the ally of a man whose exceptional good fortune is bound to expose him to many catastrophes. If some disaster overcame you, I should be obliged to come to your rescue. So let us separate, for in this way I shall be able to witness your troubles with a quiet mind.*

Later on, Polycrates, having been warned that some of his subjects were rebelling against him, wished to get rid of them as quietly as possible. He asked Cambyses, king of Persia, to give him some help.

"You must ask me," he said, "for help from my fleet and I will send you a few ships. I will see to it that the would-be rebels are in the crews. Of course, you will take care that they do not come back."

This plan was carried out by Polycrates but Cambyses apparently failed to keep his side of the bargain.

However nobody knows what *really* happened. Did the rebels get wind of the fate which was being prepared for them? Did Cambyses forget to lay his hands on them? In any case, these men escaped and set off to get help and revenge in Sparta. It appears that the rebels were so angry that they made the longest speech imaginable, so that none of their listeners could understand what they meant.

"We've forgotten what you said in the beginning," said the Spartan chiefs, "and we couldn't understand what you meant towards the end."

The rebels stated what they wanted more briefly; this time, they were promised help and support, and a Spartan fleet set sail for Samos.

Had the gods grown weary of bringing good fortune to Polycrates? Amasis followed what was happening with sorrowful interest. However, his forebodings proved to be quite wrong. The Spartans besieged Samos, but after a few minor victories, they were driven back. The siege went on for forty days, until finally the Spartans came to the conclusion that they were wasting their time. They embarked and sailed back to the mainland of Greece after wishing the outlaws good luck.

It is said—but only by scandalmongers—that their departure was determined less for military reasons than because there suddenly appeared in the Spartan camp thousands of coins stamped with the head of Polycrates. Wretched Spartans! They did not yet know what the tyrant was like, but they soon learnt by bitter experience, if it is really true that—as is said—these coins were made of lead, rolled in gold dust. Obviously Polycrates was a bad fellow. As for the outlaws, they gave up all idea of returning to their native town and they went to another island where they behaved abominably.

As for Polycrates, he got it into his head that nothing could go wrong for him; in fact, he thought he could do exactly what he liked. So for instance, when Oretes, the Persian governor of Sardis, sent him a messenger, Polycrates—who was lying down in the coolness of his house with his face turned to the wall—would not even move to listen to the herald, and would not reply to his questions. This made Oretes so angry that he swore he would ruin Polycrates.

The latter, conceited as ever, was planning to build large fleets so as to dominate the Mediterranean and enrich himself by plundering the ships of other nations on a very large scale.

When Oretes learnt of this, he sent a message to the tyrant saying: "You are making very important plans,

Polycrates, but you are not as wealthy as you would like to be. As for me, I know that King Cambyses is out to kill me and I am closely watched. If you come to fetch me, you can take away with you all my treasures and we will share them between us. You do not have to take my word for it, send a reliable friend and I will show him what I have got."

Very much excited, Polycrates immediately told his secretary, Meander, to go to Sardis. Meanwhile, Oretes filled some large chests with stones, then he covered the stones with gold dust and closed the chests with solid fastenings as if they contained the most precious valuables. Meander came, opened up the boxes, was completely taken in and made enthusiastic reports to his master.

This time Polycrates did not hesitate. Eagerly, he arranged for a large ship to be equipped for the journey and fixed the date of his departure. During the night before he left, his daughter had a most peculiar dream. She saw her father hanging up in the air, bathed by Jupiter, God of Rain, and blistered by the sun.

What a strange vision! Terrified out of her wits, she rushed off to see the tyrant and beseeched him not to go. His friends also pleaded with him, as did the priests and the seers who declared that this omen was very odd indeed, to say the least of it. Polycrates persisted. He tore himself away from them, went down to the port and climbed aboard the ship, still pursued by the lamentations of his daughter.

"Don't go, Father; don't go; something terrible will happen to you," she cried from the shore, twisting her arms and tearing her hair.

Furious, Polycrates stood on the deck whilst the moorings were loosened and the ship gradually drew away from the wharf.

Then he cursed her, crying out: "I shall punish you, you wicked creature, for trying to bring me ill luck! When I come back, I shall not seek a husband for you. You shall remain unmarried!"

The poor girl was weeping hard and she even beseeched the gods to fulfil her father's threats and let her remain unmarried, provided that he came back safe and sound.

Alas! This time the gods had really abandoned Polycrates. No sooner had he reached his destination than Oretes seized him and killed him. Afterwards, the Persian had his corpse hung up on a gallows so that it was bathed by the rain and burnt by the sun just as his daughter had seen in her dream.

A Tyrant who made Fun of Everybody

PISISTRATUS, the tyrant of Athens, was not in a good temper, for he was obliged to think about his most unpleasant situation. Ever since leaving Athens, he was preoccupied with thoughts of how on earth he could get back there. Living uncomfortably in a little country cottage, he began one day to look at his maidservant, Phya, who was bustling about the house, drawing water from the well and watering the flowerbeds.

"A really fine woman," he thought, "and tall, too, very strong with regular features, and splendid bearing. Who would imagine that she was a country girl? She is built like a goddess."

But Pisistratus did not spend too much time thinking about the girl; his attention was turned to Athens, his native city, from which he had been expelled by his enemies. However, he was not the kind of man to be depressed by defeat for long. The venerable Solon, the lawgiver of Athens, had understood this very well. He said that Pisistratus was a sly fox and he had come down to the public square to put his fellow-citizens on guard against the exiled tyrant.

"Your cowardice will be your misfortune," he cried; "you listen to his fine speeches and you do not see his real character. You live most happily under a Republic, but you will wake up one day to find that you are being dominated by a tyrant."

Still, the humbler folk of Athens liked Pisistratus. The skilled workmen, the farm labourers and the mountain shepherds had found in him a protector. The "fox" immediately took advantage of their attachment to him. He made cuts on his arms and legs, and rushed, bleeding from his wounds, to the public square.

"They tried to murder me," he cried "I must have a guard."

With shouts of devotion and yells of indignation, the people voted that he should have a guard. Pisistratus, under the safe protection of a company of stout fellows armed with bludgeons, took possession of the Acropolis, the hill which is the site of the temple of Minerva which has always been the citadel of Athens. In this way, he had become the master of the city. Old Solon hung his weapons over his door and withdrew from the outside world, his heart filled with despair.

However, in spite of all his cunning tricks, the "fox" had many powerful enemies; in particular, the noble family of the Alcmeonides whose chief, Megacles, hatched a plot against him. Pisistratus had only just had time to escape from Megacles. That was why he now found himself torn with impatience and frustration in a little country village, but he still had one or two tricks to play. All he needed was just one stroke of luck.

Indeed, that is exactly what happened. One evening, a horseman rode up to the garden gate. Phya went to fetch her master.

"Did he tell you his name?"

"No, Master, and I wouldn't know how to describe him to you. He's wrapped his face in his cloak just as if he had a toothache, so that no one could possibly have recognised him on the road."

Pisistratus, who was inclined to be suspicious, would have liked to know more about this man before seeing him. As he was crossing the courtyard, he saw the visitor's horse—a splendid creature, a real thoroughbred with well-set shoulders and a small head—which pranced about as if he had just come out of the stable.

The former tyrant adored horses and had even kept a racing stable in the past. "What a glorious mount!" he thought. Then after examining the steed very carefully, he said to himself, "He must come from the famous stud of the Alcmeonides; if I am not mistaken, Megacles is trying to outwit me."

"Come Megacles," he cried in a loud voice as he entered the room where his visitor was waiting for him, "Out with it! What do you want to see me about?"

Megacles, for it was he, did not hesitate for a moment. The different factions were quarrelling in Athens and, as he had fallen out with his friends, Megacles was trying to ally himself with Pisistratus.

"On condition," he stipulated, "that I shall have my share of the profits, you can come back to Athens, Pisistratus, but you must marry my daughter."

Pisistratus burst out laughing. "And very nice for her, too! I'm middle-aged, I've buried two wives and I've got four sons."

"My daughter knows her duty," replied the other, "She's not expecting to marry a good-looking young fellow of no importance. As long as I tell her to take you. . . ."

"Delighted, Megacles, we are in complete agreement, but there remains one little problem to solve. You are kind enough to think that I alone can re-establish order in Athens. You offer me power and I accept it with gratitude, but perhaps the people of Athens will insist on being consulted. Our fellow-citizens don't like people to take advantage of them. How do you think they are going to receive me?"

"I don't know at all, Pisistratus. It is up to you to settle all that."

"That's all very well. I don't want to return through the back door, beg to be received, and have to snivel at the Assembly. No, I want to be greeted with cheers and to come back in triumph!"

Megacles grew impatient. "Well, you'll have to come back as best you can! You don't expect the gods to come and fetch you and lead you by the hand to the Acropolis?"

"The gods! Yes, yes, Megacles, the gods!"

In the evening, the maidservant began to water the garden again. The wheel over the well creaked, the aromatic scent of the wet plants filled the night air, the pail clanked in the well. Her master's eyes followed her coming and going in the garden.

"Let me think things over a little, Megacles," he said at last, reflectively.

A few days later, Pisistratus made a solemn entry into Athens. He was preceded by an imposing procession. First of all there were horsemen, members of the noblest families, led by the Alcmeonides, on their prancing well-bred steeds. Then came the tyrant's guards, the faithful mountaineers, the sturdy workmen armed with clubs; after them, the sons of the tyrant, young men of splendid bearing; and lastly, four heralds clad in brilliant colours. At every cross-road they halted, flourishing their silver trumpets and shouting to the four corners their astonishing proclamation: "Citizens of Athens, give your warmest welcome to Pisistratus, son of Hippocrates. The Goddess Athena, who honours him more than any other mortal, is personally conducting him to her own shrine and citadel."

Then there appeared a splendid chariot inlaid with gold and ivory, drawn by the finest horses ever bred in Attica (the region round Athens). And standing on this chariot . . . Athena, daughter of Zeus! The goddess herself, the mistress of Athens, the warrior maiden whose single glance can cause death. Taller than any woman in Athens, her splendid bearing inspired respect, her noble face reflected the majesty of the gods. Her shining helmet was made by Hephaistos himself, as was her spear, and the breastplate which covered her bosom. Respectful and with downcast eyes, on the same chariot stood Pisistratus, a little behind the goddess.

Awestruck and filled with terror, the women raised their arms towards heaven and beat their heads on the ground. The street urchins uttered shrill cries. The crowd divided to make way for this procession. Had it not been said that a single glance of the gods is enough to shatter any mortal? In a flash, the goddess had passed. Pisistratus had gone up into the Acropolis, the doors of the citadel closed on him and on his faithful supporters.

"Well," he sighed, leaping down from the chariot, "All is well!" and, turning towards his divine protectress still standing on the magnificent chariot: "Now you can come down my good girl! Phya, I am pleased with you!"

We have to admit that Herodotus, who related this story in one of his books, had some reason to be astonished.

"Is it possible," he said, "that such a clumsy piece of trickery could have succeeded in outwitting the Athenians who are considered to be the most intelligent of the Greeks?"

12

The Battle goes to the Strong

OW that we have read how Cyrus, king of the Persians, triumphed over the Lydian monarch, Croesus, we must also learn how Persia grew in strength and power afterwards. All the peoples of Asia and even the Egyptians obeyed the king of Persia, for his empire extended from India to the Aegean Sea. Throughout the world he was called the Great King, or just simply the King, for he was unrivalled in might and in influence. His empire was so great that several towns quarrelled for the honour of providing the royal residence. Usually he lived in Susa, in a palace of the greatest splendour. Every kind of luxury was displayed at his court, which was magnificent because of his boundless wealth.

His messengers travelled on splendid roads, bearing his orders to the remotest provinces which were governed by his officials. These satraps and inspectors—"the eyes

A splendid chariot appeared

and the ears of the King"—kept a watchful eye on the administration of the empire.

This immense territory could provide endless numbers of soldiers and limitless wealth; each year, fourteen thousand five hundred and sixty talents were paid into the treasury.

Of course, the Greek cities of Ionia in Asia Minor obeyed the king of the Persians, but they were often inclined to be rebellious and took every opportunity to be a nuisance to their master. It happened that a very cunning Greek, who was named Histiaeus and was tyrant of the town of Miletus, was detained by the king of Persia in Susa. He had the very peculiar idea of suggesting to the people of Miletus that they should revolt, hoping that Darius, the king, would send him to crush the rebellion and that he would thus have an opportunity to escape.

He found the most ingenious means of sending a message to Miletus. He shaved off the hair of a slave and tattooed on his head the word *Rebel*. When the hair had grown again, he sent him to Miletus, ordering him to have his head shaved as soon as he arrived. So it was that the people of Miletus were foolish enough to rebel against Darius, king of the Persians, inciting the other Ionian towns to follow their example, and starting a war which nearly brought about the destruction of Greece.

Aristagoras of Miletus rushed off to ask for help from the Greeks of the mainland who were, of course, of his race. The Spartans turned him down, but Athens was bold enough to listen to him. Twenty Athenian triremes (galleys with three banks of oars) set off for Ionia; the Athenians landed, and succeeded in progressing, unopposed, as far as Sardis, the former capital of Croesus.

6

They captured the town and burnt it down, quite use-lessly, for a Persian army came up soon after, defeated the Greeks and scattered their forces.

Darius immediately set out to punish the rebellion in Ionia, though he did not pay it much more attention than any of the other revolts which occurred from time to time in his empire. However, he was really scandalised by the intervention of the Athenians—a nation so insignificant that he was obliged to ask who they were. When he was told, he seized a bow, shot an arrow straight into the air and said: "May the gods grant me full vengeance against the Athenians."

Henceforth, at each meal, a servant had to repeat to him: "Lord, remember the Athenians."

Soon Darius resolved to make an end of these insolent Athenians, and also of all the other Greeks who were so restless and so ready to help the men of their race estab-lished in Asia. He raised an army and ordered his generals to bring back all the citizens of Athens in chains. Every-body believed that this would be quite easy, for a struggle between the king of a huge empire and the citizens of a small town could not fail to be uneven!

Two Persian armies—one arriving by sea and the other by land—invaded Greece from the north and encoun-tered scarcely any resistance. As soon as the Athenians were told of what was happening, they prepared to fight without any kind of hesitation. Of course, they tried to find allies and they thought, first of all, of Sparta, the only town on a level with Athens. They chose a profes-sional herald—that is to say, a messenger in the service of the state—who was one of the swiftest and one of the most skilful. His name has come down to us through the ages: it was Philippides. He set off hurriedly and completed the journey in five days, which was record time, although he had a very odd adventure on the way.

As he was crossing a range of mountains, he came across a little man with a horned head, who was playing a cheerful tune on his pipe.

"Philippides," said this peculiar shepherd, "ask your fellow-citizens why they have not honoured me. I have no temple in their city, and yet I am a kindly god, and at this very moment I am ready to be most useful to you."

Then he disappeared into the woods. The herald realised that he had met Pan. When he told his story on his return, the Athenians decided to build the god a little sanctuary on the slopes of the Acropolis, for they were not in a position to neglect anyone who could help them.

Philippides had certainly done his best in Sparta. The idea of sending an army to Athens appealed to the Spartans. They said that it would be better to wait a little, because it was the ninth day of the month and their laws forbade them to send out an army before the full moon.

All the same they wished the Athenians every kind of success in the coming war. Philippides wondered if the Spartans had not been making fun of him and if the delay in the departure of their army was due to something else besides the phases of the moon.

In these circumstances, the Athenians had no choice but to surrender or to fight. They decided on the latter course and sent their forces to a small plain in the north of Attica called Marathon.

At the very last minute, reinforcements came from

Plataea, a little city which had never distinguished herself before. However, the action of her contingent on that particular day was destined to make her immortal.

For their part, the Persians had landed and drawn up their forces in battle order. In their ranks there was an Athenian deserter, named Hippias, who was a son of Pisistratus. He hoped that the Persians would place Athens under his rule. He was already quite elderly; his treachery was a disgrace to his white hairs.

Among the ten officers who commanded the Athenian army was a peculiar fellow called Miltiades. He was not particularly young and he was of Athenian origin, but he came from the land of the Chersonese, where he governed a small state. He loved the land of his ancestors and was ready to prove it.

For a while, the Athenian generals were doubtful as to whether they should fight, for the odds against them seemed so great! A few of them, however, were more courageous; among them was Miltiades. After a council of war in which he expressed his opinion very firmly, the Greeks decided to fight with Miltiades as their leader.

When at last dawn came on the 13th September in the year 490 B.C., an intense heat spread over the barren plain as soon as the sun had risen. The Athenians extended their front as widely as the ranks of the Persians opposite them. The Greek forces were so spread out that there was a weakness in the centre, though the reinforcements from Plataea filled up the left wing. The Athenians were engaged against a Persian army for the first time, but the many-coloured clothes and the peculiar weapons of this Asiatic horde did not frighten them. At a given signal, the Greeks rushed forward to charge the Barbarians, although the distance between the two armies was two-thirds of a mile. They ran quickly so as to reduce the time in which they were exposed to the arrows of the enemy.

The violence of the Greek onslaught disconcerted the Persians who had thought that they would themselves attack an enemy formed into solid squares. Nevertheless, the best Persian troops were in the centre, and these resisted so well that they broke the ranks of the Athenians. But in the wings, however, the Greeks were victorious. Closing in, they came to the help of their comrades and routed the Persians.

The latter fell back in disorder towards their fleet which was at anchor not very far from the shore. Flushed with their victory, the Athenians rushed towards the sea and tried to prevent the Persians from re-embarking. They were not successful in this manœuvre, but they were able to destroy seven large enemy galleys. It was then that the brother of the dramatist Aeschylus met with a glorious death.

He seized hold of the gunwale of an enemy ship with his right hand; but a Persian soldier cut his hand off. Immediately, he gripped the rail with his left hand, this was also cut off. Then, according to tradition, he then used his teeth, and his head was cut off to make him let go.

All danger had not yet been averted. A contingent of Persians had left the army before the battle and sailed on towards Athens, hoping to take the city by surprise. In eight hours' forced marching, the Athenian warriors gained Athens although they were weary after the battle. So the enemy found the city well defended, and the

Persian fleet, anchored in the bay, remained for a few days and then sailed off towards Asia.

Greece was saved.

Nothing can describe the joy of the warriors on the night of the battle of Marathon. Whilst their generals busied themselves in seeing that the dead were properly buried so that their souls should be assured of immortality, a messenger set off for Athens. He was a well-known athelete who had often been victor in the running races. In the course of a night he covered the distance between Marathon and Athens, without stopping. After passing through the gates, he knocked at the doors of all the leading citizens. He announced the great news to all of them, and then he fell dead.

It is only fair to add that two thousand Spartans arrived in Athens just after the battle. They were warmly thanked and, at their request, they were taken to the battlefield so that they could see how many Persians had fallen.

13

Everything Belongs to Kings
except the Wind

ARIUS became very angry when he heard about the defeat of his generals at Marathon. He could not bring himself to believe that so small a nation would challenge his might a second time, and he began to raise a new army. He intended to command it himself and he appointed his son Xerxes to administer the empire in his absence. But Darius died in 485 B.C., and Xerxes succeeded him.

This king had, first of all, to suppress the Egyptians who had rebelled against him. Then, as soon as he had settled this business, he continued the preparations for war with the Greeks. It is said that he spent four years recruiting troops and accumulating the supplies required to feed so great an army; even thousands of men are useless if they are dying of thirst and hunger. In fact, the king knew that the countries they had to cross were too poor to feed them. He levied among his allies and among the nations he had conquered, infantrymen, cavalry, archers, sailors, warships, transports, food and metals. Last of all, in order to facilitate the passage of his troops, he commissioned two of the greatest enterprises imaginable: a canal across the isthmus of Mount Athos and a bridge of boats to pass over the Hellespont.

The easiest way to come from Asia to Europe is to cross this narrow strait which we call the Dardanelles, and which was known to the Greeks as the Hellespont. The army of Xerxes could not avoid passing over this strip of sea. The king, therefore, ordered his men to tie flat, broad boats together with ropes made from the fibre of bulrushes and linen, so as to make an improvised bridge, capable of taking the weight of men and horses.

As soon as the army reached Europe, the land forces were to continue on their way by following the coast, whilst the fleet would accompany them by sailing not far from the shore. However, the ships would have to circumnavigate the mountainous peninsula of Athos which projects far into the sea and is linked to the mainland by a narrow isthmus. A Persian fleet had already been badly battered by the wind in this vicinity.

Because of this previous experience, the great king imagined that the gods of Athos were hostile to him, and that his fleet would be wrecked for a second time against the steep cliffs of the promontory. It was for this reason that he had a canal cut through the isthmus, wide enough for two warships to sail side by side. Each end was to be protected by a stone pier to prevent the channel becoming silted up with sand.

To carry out this great project, thousands of people were deported from their homes and made to dig ceaselessly, driven on by the whips of their overseers. The sides of the canal kept falling in and the work had to be done again and again. The Phoenicians alone were intelligent enough to cut their section of the trench much wider at the top than at the bottom, so that the banks did not keep on crumbling. This is what peoples under the sway of Xerxes had to put up with in order to satisfy his despotic whims. The worthy Herodotus, who tells this story, declares that the king who commissioned this immense work, only wanted to display the extent of his might, because ships could have been dragged *over* the isthmus instead of passing through a canal.

Naturally, the Greeks knew exactly what was happening. Three Greek spies had been sent to Sardis, the place from which the king directed operations. They were discovered, tortured and were about to be executed, when Xerxes was informed and he intervened to save them.

"They must be shown everything," he said disdainfully; "let them review our infantry and cavalry and then set them free. When the Greeks are told of the dangers they have to face, they will submit without having to be attacked."

The Spartan Demaratus was in Susa and he, too, wished to inform his fellow-citizens of what was happening, but he feared that his messenger might be caught and searched. He therefore devised a trick similar to the one contrived by Histiaeus of Miletus ten years previously. He took two of the wooden tablets covered with wax which were then used instead of writing-paper. He removed the wax, engraved his message on the wood and then covered it once more with a layer of wax. He then sealed up the tablets and he sent them off to Sparta. The members of the council were very much perplexed when they saw these blank writing tablets, but a woman, Gorgo, wife of Leonidas who was at that time king of the country, settled their problem.

"Scrape off the wax," she said; "I am sure that there is a message beneath it."

And this was done.

When the army had collected at Sardis and Xerxes was preparing to set off, a fateful piece of news reached his ears: the bridge of boats which had been placed at such expense across the Hellespont had just been wrecked. Scarcely had it been finished when the wind blew with great violence; the rough sea snapped the binding, broke up the bridge and swallowed up the boats. The king was infuriated when he learnt of this disaster and he gave orders that the Hellespont should receive three hundred lashes and have a pair of handcuffs thrown into it whilst these words were shouted out: "O sea, this punishment is being inflicted on you by my master whom you have harmed, although he has done nothing to offend you; whether you wish it or not, he and his armies will cross your waters."

Perhaps he was being less unfair when he ordered the execution of all those who had planned the construction of the bridge!

Nevertheless, after all this, the bridge had to be rebuilt. This time, two bridges were made and every precaution was taken. Since the engineers were very anxious to limit the risks to the king and to themselves, they positioned their boats with due allowance for the flow of the tides and currents, and they calculated the length of the chains holding down the anchors according to the direction of the winds. They also had special cables made to link the boats together, composed of two-thirds papyrus to one-third of flax. On the bridge thus prepared they laid beams and then planks. On this wood they poured earth and, on either side, they raised up parapets so that the horses would not be able to see the waves.

The flowers of the spring of 480 B.C. bloomed. Xerxes left Sardis and advanced towards the sea. Half his army marched in front of him and the other half behind. In the centre, separated from the rest of the troops by a long interval, came a thousand picked Persian cavalry; then a thousand foot soldiers, with the heads of their spears pointing to the ground; then ten sacred horses of the breed which the Persians called Nisaean and which surpassed in beauty those of every other strain; then the Chariot of God—empty, since no mortal may sit in it—with a charioteer on foot behind, holding the reins; then lastly, the king himself in a chariot drawn by ten Nisaean horses. The rest of the bodyguard followed him; among them were ten thousand men whose spears had gold or silver pomegranates on the butt.

Xerxes installed himself in the land of Abydos at the top of a hill where a terrace of white stone had been constructed. Sitting there, he admired the splendid spectacle of his army and his fleet.

"I am happy," he said.

Nevertheless, he began to weep. Artabanus, his uncle, asked him why he was so sad.

"I am sorry for these men," said Xerxes; "see how

many of them there are; yet, in a hundred years' time, not one will be alive."

"Ah," replied Artabanus, "there are sadder things than that. Life is often so tragic that death seems rather to represent a sure refuge. To tell the truth, it is not that question which troubles me. I fear for you two perils which are due to the very size of your forces. First of all, your ships are so numerous that they will find it hard to discover an anchorage in which they may all shelter; and storms are often stronger than men. On the other hand, your soldiers may not be able to live off the land; the further you go from your bases the more they are in danger of famine."

These were wise words. Xerxes thanked his uncle courteously and sent him back to Susa to govern the empire during his absence.

On the next day, before dawn, incense was burnt on the great bridge, and the road was strewn with flowers. Then, as the first rays of the sun made the water gleam with light, Xerxes took a gold cup and poured libations of wine into the sea which he had previously chastised. He prayed to the God of the Hellespont to grant him victory in the coming campaign. Then he threw into the waves, with the gold cup, a large golden bowl and a Persian sword encrusted with jewels. Doubtless, he was filled with remorse and fear that he had offended the mighty waters.

Then the army crossed the bridge and the king himself passed over it. For seven days and seven nights the Persian troops marched, urged on with whips. All the peoples of the empire had been forced to send contingents. The Persians and the Medes wore felt caps, coats of mail and cloaks of many colours. Their weapons were a short spear, a large bow and a sword slung to their belts. The Assyrians wore helmets of strips of bronze woven together in a curious manner; in their hands they carried wooden clubs, studded with iron points; and, following a very old tradition, instead of metal breastplates, they wore tunics made of many layers of thick woven linen, so tightly woven that swords glanced from their surface.

The Dacians were armed with a kind of battle-axe called *sagaris*, and the troops from India were archers clad in cotton which was considered by the people of the Ancient World to be a curiosity and called by them "tree wool". Then came certain tribes from the shores of the Caspian Sea, some dressed in goatskins, whilst others wore clothes of dazzling colours.

The soldiers from Thrace wore caps of fox fur and top-boots of doeskin. The Chalybes from the shores of the Black Sea were protected by bronze helmets surmounted by plumes and by the horns and ears of an ox worked in metal. The Mosches wore wooden headgear. The Mares were armed with stakes. There were many more contingents besides these, but the most spectacular of all came from the furthermost parts of the empire. These were the Arabs—archers covered from head to foot in cloaks of wool—and the negroes who wore the skins of lions and panthers wrapped round their loins. Their bows were made from the ribs of palm leaves and they were used to shoot arrows with flint heads. When they marched to battle their bodies were covered with white and crimson paint and they threw javelins tipped with the horns of gazelles.

When this flood of men had swept past, Xerxes ordered

them to be counted. Ten thousand men at a time would be collected and huddled together as closely as possible, and a circle was traced around them. After they had gone, a low wall was built on the circumference. Then as many men as possible were crowded into the enclosure. Thus the soldiers of Xerxes were counted in groups of ten thousand.

How many men were there? The historians of Antiquity quote unbelievable figures: one million seven hundred thousand, said Herodotus. We have good reason to believe that he exaggerated but the fact remains that it was a huge army. When it advanced across the wild lands of Thrace and Thessaly, the waters of the rivers were dried up simply because of the great number of soldiers who took their water supply from them.

14

"Here, Obedient to their Laws, We Lie"

HIS river of men swept on towards the Greeks, who were trying to organise their defences. The Athenians knew that they were in the greatest danger because they had beaten the Persians at Marathon, so they tried to gather the other Greek cities around them. This was a difficult task, not only because of age-old rivalries, but also because the Greek states realised that vast numbers of soldiers were being mobilised by Xerxes and many of them thought it was wiser to submit. Some people advised the Athenians to abandon Athens without a struggle and to create a new city in a remote country where the Persians would not be able to attack them. Nevertheless, many of the cities of the Peloponnesus, including Sparta, prepared to resist. These allied states then sought the help of Gelon, the powerful tyrant of Syracuse.

The latter was ready to send two hundred ships, twenty thousand infantrymen, two thousand men of the heavy cavalry, two thousand archers, two thousand slingers, two thousand light horsemen and supplies for the whole duration of the war, on condition that he was created commander-in-chief of the allied army.

"Menelaus would turn in his grave," was the reply, "at the idea that the Spartans might give the command of their forces to a man from Syracuse."

"Very well," replied Gelon; "I am most patient and reasonable; give me the command of the fleet instead."

"We don't need a general or an admiral. We need an army," replied the Athenians. "We are of too ancient a race to give up the command of the fleet which is ours by tradition."

"As you wish then," said Gelon. "You may be short of men, but you seem to have plenty of generals. Go back to Greece and tell your fellow-citizens that they have missed a wonderful chance to double the strength of their army."

On their return, the allied leaders decided to protect Attica by defending the pass of Thermopylae. Meanwhile, the Greek fleet would await the arrival of the Persian sea forces near Cape Artemisium, not far away. Most people imagine that Thermopylae is a rocky gorge, but it is really a narrow neck of marshy land, stretching between a mountain range and the sea. The hot springs which have given the region its name gush out of the ground and the pass is so narrow in certain places that a half-ruined wall was enough to close the gap. Whilst waiting for the Persians, the Greeks hurriedly rebuilt this wall.

The Persians fell in their thousands

There were three thousand eight hundred soldiers who had come from different cities, a thousand men from Phocis and an unknown number of Locrians. Lastly, King Leonidas the descendant of Hercules, brought with him three hundred picked Spartans.

When the coming of the Persians was announced, the men of this tiny army began to feel panic-stricken. Most of the leaders thought it would be better to retire to the isthmus of Corinth so that the Peloponnesus at least could be adequately defended. But Leonidas, thinking of the people whom they would leave a prey to the Persians, decided to make a stand at Thermopylae itself. Shortly afterwards, a mounted Persian scout came up to find out the approximate strength of the Greek forces. He saw the Spartans who were on duty near the wall. They had stacked their weapons against the ramparts; some of them were naked and indulging in gymnastic exercises and others were combing their long hair. He counted them slowly and went off. None of them had even troubled to glance at him.

Xerxes could not believe that this handful of men was preparing to resist. Nevertheless, he questioned a deserter named Demaratus.

"Prince," replied the latter. "I am sure that these men are determined to fight, for it is the custom among the Spartans to groom their hair carefully when there is likely to be great danger."

Xerxes allowed four days to pass without taking action; he believed that the Greeks would withdraw. On the fifth day, he was seized with rage and launched some of his troops against them. The Greeks were at an advantage because of the narrowness of the pass, their great knowledge of warfare and their superb courage, so they defended themselves successfully. Then Xerxes sent out his picked troops. They were called the Immortals because as soon as one soldier fell, another immediately took his place.

It is said that the king, who was watching the battle, was so anxious about the fate of his soldiers, that he descended from his throne three times. The next day, the Persians were again driven back and Xerxes became extremely anxious.

It was at this point that a Greek traitor named Ephialtes, who knew the country very well, promised the king that if he were rewarded, he would show the Persian soldiers a way round the mountain which came out at the rear of the pass. As night fell (according to Herodotus, the soldiers in their tents were lighting their lamps), the Immortals left the Persian camp and followed Ephialtes, crossing a little torrent and then climbing over the crest of the mountain. Dawn came as they reached its summit; owing to the dense woods, they were able to march unseen.

There they came upon a thousand Greek soldiers—the men of Phocis who had volunteered to protect the flank of the Greek army by keeping guard over the pass. They had been aroused at the very last moment by the crackling of the dry leaves in the woods, and had hurriedly rushed forward. The Persians overwhelmed them with arrows and javelins; the Phocians scattered and, hiding behind rocks, they lay in wait for a second attack. The attack never came. Without paying any attention to the Phocians, the Persians descended on Thermopylae.

By now, Leonidas had realised what was happening.

It is said that the seer Megistias was the first to warn the Spartans that they were destined to die on that day. Then, even before dawn, some Persian deserters had come to Leonidas and told him that he had been out-flanked. Lastly, Greek scouts, stationed in the mountains, perceived the Immortals advancing and hurried to bear the news to their chief.

Leonidas understood that all was lost. Those who made a stand here were bound to die; it would be wiser to pre-serve the scanty number of valuable soldiers to continue the defence of Greece. He therefore ordered all the allies from different parts of the country to withdraw. As for himself, he could not and would not abandon the post which had been entrusted to him; this applied just as much to his three hundred men, for such was the law of Sparta. Honour forbade them to do anything else but die where they stood.

It is said that the soldiers from Thespiae refused to obey the order to withdraw and insisted on sharing the fate of the Spartans. Leonidas also forced a contingent from Thebes to remain as hostages—the Thebans were suspected of being traitors and in the pay of the Persians. As for the seer Megistias, nothing would induce him to desert the others so he contented himself by sending off his only son who had been fighting by his side during the previous combats.

At dawn, Xerxes poured out libations to the rising sun and offered up prayers to his gods. Then he waited a while, for the time he had fixed with Ephialtes had not yet arrived. The signal was given a little later on in the morning—"at the hour when the market places begin to fill," as Herodotus declared. Alas, how far they were

from those peaceful occupations of the everyday world;
all that was left to them was to sell their lives as dearly as
possible! More than one of these men must have turned
his thoughts to his home, to his children, to his fields, to
everything that he loved so dearly and would see no more.
The Barbarians discharged so many arrows that a soldier
protested that they were veiling the rays of the sun,
whereupon a Spartan cried out: "So much the better!
We shall fight in the shade."

The Persians attacked in successive waves. Numerous,
but ill-trained and far from courageous, they fell in their
thousands. Their officers rallied them with whips and
drove them on to battle once more. Many died, trodden
under foot by their comrades. Soon, among the Greeks,
lances and spears were broken and they fought on with
their blunted swords. Leonidas fell; a terrible combat was
waged over his body. Four times the Spartans recaptured
his body, and four times they were driven back, but not
without having killed two of the Persian king's brothers
who had taken part in the assault.

When the Immortals descended on Thermopylae, the
Greeks withdrew from the wall and retired to a hillock
to make their final stand.

The Thebans, whom the Spartans had detained by
force, managed to escape. They surrendered to the king
who ordered them to be branded like slaves.

At that moment a strange reinforcement reached the
Greeks. A Spartan who had withdrawn to a village,
because of an infection which had blinded him, learnt of
the desperate plight of his comrades. He forced his slave
to hand him his weapons and to lead him to the field of
battle. Once there, the slave fled whilst the blind man

sought death by throwing himself into the thickest of the battle. Finally, having knocked down the wall, the Barbarians surrounded the Spartans on all sides. Some of the survivors were even defending themselves with their bare fists.

Later on, the Greeks erected a stone lion on the hill where the last stand had been made. Columns were also set up on the battlefield and on the one inscribed with the names of the dead Spartans was written the following epitaph:

> *Go, tell the Spartans, thou who passest by,*
> *that here, obedient to their laws, we lie.*

15

Zeus gives the Athenians Wooden Walls

FTER the fall of Thermopylae, the situation of the Greeks was not as desperate as might have been imagined. The fleet had succeeded in holding up the advance of the Persian ships in a battle which would otherwise have been considered indecisive.

Nevertheless, there appeared to be no way of saving Athens itself, since the road by land was open to the enemy forces and terror reigned in the city. The military leaders could not make up their minds what to do, and the people repeated the words of the Oracle about the fate of their country.

When they had heard about the preparations for invasion, the Athenians had, of course, sent messengers to Delphi. As soon as she saw them seated in the temple, the Pythia made a most terrifying prophecy.

"Why do you sit down, you unfortunate men?" she cried to them; "you must flee to the furthest parts of the earth, abandon your dwellings and the hills of your city. . . . The temples of the immortals will be given up to violence and will be razed to the ground. To-day they are shaken by terror, and floods of dark blood flow from the rooftops."

The Athenians, terrified, threw themselves on the ground and pressed their faces against the earth. On seeing this, a certain Timon, a citizen of Delphi, advised them to take olive branches, as do petitioners, and to question the Oracle a second time. This they did, imploring their gods to give them a more encouraging reply.

Then the Pythia explained: "Athena cannot appease Zeus in spite of her prayers. I tell you this for the second time and my prophecy remains unchanged.

"Of all that is contained within the frontiers of Athens, Zeus will give Athena only impregnable walls of wood. . . ." Then she added, "Oh Salamis, how many men will be made to perish by you!"

Terrified as they were by the threat to their existence, the Athenians excitedly discussed the words of the Oracle. Where were these walls of wood? Some thought that the Pythia referred to the Acropolis which had formerly been surrounded by a palisade. Consequently, a number of citizens, for the most part poor and very ignorant, built a fence of planks around it and took refuge within the enclosure. Most people thought that the ships of the fleet were the "wooden walls" of Athens.

In any case, it was obviously mere common sense to evacuate the city. The officials issued a proclamation declaring that people should seek refuge for their families wherever possible. With despair in their hearts, the Athenians transferred women and children to the islands off the coast of Attica, to Aegina or to Salamis, both of which are quite near the capital.

Having taken this melancholy step, each Athenian went back to his post in the fleet which was anchored in the straits of Salamis, whilst the Persian fleet was manœuvring in the open sea towards Phaleron. Three months had passed since the army of Xerxes had crossed the Hellespont.

Of Athens there remained absolutely nothing. The lower town was occupied without resistance, and the Persian troops took up their position opposite the Acropolis on the little hill called the Areopagus; from there, tying strips of burning tow to their arrows, they set fire to the wretched wall of planks. The besieged defended themselves with the courage of despair, rolling down great blocks of stone from the top of the fortress, but some bold Persians climbed up a steep slope and killed many of them. A few survivors took refuge in the ancient temple of Athena, but the Persians broke in at the gates and massacred everyone they found inside. Then they plundered and burnt the citadel. The ancient monuments of Athens were destroyed, so were the most revered of her treasures; even the sacred olive tree, which had appeared at the bidding of Athena, was burnt down.

The Greek deserters whom Xerxes brought in his train, were installed in Athens. No mention would be made of these shameful characters, were it not for the fact that they handed down to us an exciting and wonderful legend. Whilst two of these scoundrels were walking across the deserted and ravaged plain near Athens, they saw a cloud of dust arrive in the direction of Eleusis.

"What can that be?" said one. It looked as if there were thousands of men on the march.

At the same instant a loud cry was heard: "Iacchos, Iacchos!"

"My friend," replied the other Greek, "something supernatural is happening. You know, of course, that it is at Eleusis that the Athenians celebrate the feast of the great goddesses Demeter and Kore. 'Iacchos' is the cry that is uttered on these occasions. Listen! the goddesses must be coming to the help of Athens."

"Silence," muttered the first Greek, "let us say nothing to the king about this miracle. We might pay for it with our lives; so let us not meddle in the affairs of the gods."

In the meantime, great confusion prevailed among the officers of the Greek fleet. Terrified by the fate of Athens which was blazing in the distance, the men of the different Peloponnesian states only thought of returning to their homes to defend their native cities. They were hastily fortifying the isthmus of Corinth; even then, a number of captains were about to give the order to set sail, when the Athenians made one last effort to restrain them.

The Athenian fleet was commanded by Themistocles who, for the past ten years, had played an important part in the administration of Athens. He believed, with good reason, that the future and the safety of Athens depended on her fleet. It was through him that the silver from the mines—which had just been discovered—was used to cover the cost of building warships. For the time being,

Thermistocles was convinced that, with the help of the Peloponnesians, the Athenian fleet was capable of holding up the Persians.

So he discussed the situation with the Peloponnesians, and more especially with Eurybiades, the Spartan commander-in-chief of the fleet, who wished to withdraw. Themistocles went on board his flagship and, with great patience and energy, succeeded in persuading the latter to hold one more council of war in which the different allies would be represented.

Nothing could have been more dramatic than these last discussions held whilst the flames and smoke were still rising from the ruins of Athens, as fresh reinforcements kept on joining the ships of the enemy fleet the masts of which were outlined on the horizon. In the meantime, the women and children stood on the shores of the islands, their hearts full of anguish, hoping that some miracle would save their country from destruction.

"Our enemies," said Themistocles, "have thousands of ships and therefore need a huge area in which to manœuvre. Let us force them to fight in the narrow straits which separate Salamis from the mainland, and they will lose the advantages they have over us."

Themistocles used all the energy, cunning and patience at his disposal in order to convince his listeners of the soundness of his idea. Nevertheless, he was furious when one of the Corinthian leaders shouted out at him: "That's enough, Themistocles; you've no right to suggest anything since your country has ceased to exist; as for you, Eurybiades, you may be our admiral, but I forbid you to entertain the suggestions of a homeless man."

He had gone too far; Themistocles could scarcely restrain his anger, but he pulled himself together and found the final answer.

"Eurybiades, if you do not listen to what I say, we, the Athenians, will embark our women and children on our ships and set off for Italy. Without our help, the Peloponnesians will have the greatest difficulty in defending themselves against the invaders."

Eurybiades was frightened and gave way. It was decided that they would fight the Persians in the straits of Salamis. Themistocles thought that he had got his own way but his troubles were not yet over.

A few hours later, the Persian fleet advanced in full battle order. Once again, there was panic among the Greeks, but there was still time for them to sail away. Once again, a council of war was held; this time Themistocles was outvoted.

Then he took a desperate decision. Night was falling and so, on leaving the council, he sent off Sicinnus— one of his most trusted followers—to the Persian headquarters.

This is what he said: "The Athenian general Themistocles has sent me to you as he wishes to gain the friendship of the king. He would like him to know that the Greeks are about to flee and that their ships will scatter. If you hurry, you may still stop them. As they are quarrelling among themselves, nothing can be easier for you than to master them."

On due consideration, the Persians believed Sicinnus and acted accordingly.

Late that night, whilst the Greek leaders were still discussing the situation, an Athenian refugee from Aegina came up to the flagship and asked to speak to Themistocles.

Previously, they had been on the worst of terms, but now he said, "Themistocles, let us forget our differences of opinion until better times. It is useless to think any more about taking flight. Our fleet is hemmed in by the enemy. I have seen it with my own eyes. That is what I have come to tell you."

"You could not have said anything which would please me more," cried Themistocles. "It is I who have induced the Barbarians to attack. Come in and tell everybody what is happening. If I say so myself, no one will believe me."

So there was nothing for it but to fight; orders to this effect were given to all the captains of the fleet. Already it was dawn, dawn on 25th September, 480 B.C.

Themistocles went from ship to ship in a small boat, encouraging the crews to fight bravely for the safety of their homes and families.

The battle that ensued was described by the great poet Aeschylus in the following words:

"When the white horses of the day scattered over the earth, bringing with them the dazzling light of the morning, the sound of cheerful voices rose from among the Greeks and was echoed by the neighbouring cliffs. No, it was not in order to flee that the Greeks sang this solemn hymn of glory, but to rush to the battle with their hearts filled with courage whilst the resounding clamour of the bugles spread like a flame from ship to ship. 'Ye sons of Greece, go and deliver your Fatherland, deliver your children and your wives, the sanctuaries which harbour the gods of your race and the tombs of your ancestors. To-day everything that you love and believe in is at stake.' As the sound of trumpets died down, the first Greek ship sped towards the Persian fleet.

"As for Xerxes, seated on a throne erected on the slopes of a hill, he followed every movement of the battle. At his feet sat his scribes, noting the names of those of his captains who distinguished themselves by their bravery. Alas for the great king! Only a short time elapsed before the Persian fleet, encumbered by the great numbers of its ships, was overwhelmed by disaster.

"Hulls capsized and the surface of the sea was covered with a tangle of wreckage and drowning men; beaches, rocks, and reefs were strewn with dead. Just as if they were spearing tunny fish caught in their nets, the Greeks destroyed their enemies, beating them down into the water with their oars, stabbing them with long spears or thrusting them back with pieces of wreckage. A long murmur made up of mingled moans and cries of pain rose up from the sea until the hour when the darkness of night brought everything to an end."

PART THREE

STORIES OF PERICLES, ALCIBIADES, SOCRATES AND DEMOSTHENES

16

The Triumphs and Sorrows of Pericles

LAUGHED at because of his curious appearance, the most celebrated of all Athenians was certainly not very handsome. It is true that he was tall and well built, but his head was so curiously shaped that it looked like an onion. Because of this every portrait of this great man represents him with a helmet on his head. For the whole of his life, he had to put up with the jokes of comedians who made fun of his odd looks.

Pericles was rich and learned. He spoke with so much charm and intelligence that he was nicknamed the Olympian Zeus. He was so popular with the citizens of Athens that they elected him commander-in-chief of the armed forces and head of the state. They re-elected him every year and kept him in this important position to the day of his death.

Pericles had the greatest respect for the people who had chosen him for such high office and who could, at any moment, dismiss him. He knew that even the poorest Athenians—the cobblers, the piemen and the small-holders of the surrounding countryside—were proud of being the citizens of the noblest of Greek towns, of being able to choose their rulers, and of voting for their own laws. They knew also that no one could remain in power without their support.

In any case, Pericles behaved with the greatest caution.

From the day he was elected, he gave up all forms of social life—such as, for instance, the racing and the banquets which were the favourite occupations of the rich Athenians. Even if he did sometimes go to the weddings of his relatives, he always went away when the guests began to get rather too merry because of the good wine they had consumed. The dignity of the head of state could not be upheld, according to Pericles, in the midst of noisy festivities where the guests tended to become too familiar with each other.

Although he was extremely eloquent, he did not like to address the council of state more often than was absolutely necessary, because he thought that in doing so he might lose his influence. That is why his enemies had nicknamed him the Galley of Salamis, comparing him with the finest vessel in the fleet. The perfection of this galley earned it a name which evoked the greatest of Athenian sea victories. It was greatly prized and was only brought out of port on very solemn occasions.

Pericles, who was so proud by nature, cultivated patience and gentleness in his contacts with other people. One morning when he was strolling in the Agora—the main square of Athens—where every citizen came at least once a day to gossip, to collect the news or to shop, a common fellow began to insult him in every possible way.

"Onion head!" cried he. "Scoundrel, give us back the money that you have taken from public funds." (Pericles had taken nothing, but the Greeks were inclined to think that their statesmen helped themselves to the money provided by taxes.) "Drunkard! You buy the votes of the electors, you pay the public orators to sing your praises. You would like to become our tyrant, and be the governor of the king of the Persians. . . ."

"Master," said the great man's slaves, "will you let us deal with this wicked fellow?"

"Pericles," cried his friends, "are you deaf? Why do you let this madman insult you so?"

"Please leave him alone, I don't even listen to what he is saying," replied the statesman. "In this our city, everyone may say what he likes. After all, we are not in Sparta where people are afraid to utter a word. Let him insult me if it gives him any kind of pleasure."

So with the greatest of calmness, Pericles strolled round the Agora, made a few purchases, talked to some of his friends and gathered the latest news; and, when the sun rose high in the sky and the heat grew intense, he called on a friend and took his midday meal with him in the coolness of an arbour.

The madman, annoyed at not having been able to make his victim lose his temper, sat down in the doorway and grumblingly waited until the statesman came out.

"Leave him alone," Pericles commanded his servants who were preparing to beat the tiresome wretch.

When Pericles came out again, the man was still there and began once more to plague him with insults. Wherever the statesman went, the drunkard followed him and continued to shout at him. Night came, and Pericles returned home. Behind him came the annoying fellow, tired out, but still abusive. Standing in front of the door of his house, the great man waited a moment. Limping, breathless and covered with dust, the lunatic caught up with him at last.

"Scoundrel! Crook! Thief!" cried the pest once more, shaking his fist.

Pericles looked at him with pity and genuine gentleness. Then, turning to his slaves who were waiting for him in a semi-circle, he said to one of them: "Take a torch and see that this citizen gets safely home."

Under the rule of Pericles, Athens became one of the most prosperous cities of all time. Whilst the Athenian ships ranged the seas bringing back rich cargo, and kept their colonies and allies in order, Pericles supervised the building of a marvellous collection of monuments on the sacred hill of the Acropolis in honour of its own goddess, Athena who was great in war and peace and the patroness of industry.

To build the splendid temple to Athena—called the Parthenon—Pericles employed the architect Ictinus, and Phidias, one of the greatest sculptors that ever lived. To accomplish this great task, they collected skilled workmen of all types: masons, carpenters, blacksmiths, stone-cutters, carvers and many more besides. Spirit-level in hand, the engineers calculated the subtle curves which would produce the most impressive perspectives. The sculptor's chisels carved a frieze out of marble. It showed the procession carrying the veil embroidered by the most distinguished young girls of the town, the veil which was a gift for the goddess.

One of the craftsmen, the most skilful of them all, fell from the top of a high scaffold and, as there seemed to be no hope of his recovering, Pericles was heartbroken. There is a tradition that the goddess appeared in a dream and told the wounded man of a remedy which saved his life. What better proof could there be that the gods themselves gave their blessing to all this work undertaken in their honour? Filled with gratitude, Pericles ordered a bronze statue of Athena the Healer to be made and had it placed on the Acropolis. Finally, inside the Parthenon there was placed a splendid statue of Athena by Phidias. It was made of ivory and gold and she had a helmet on her head, held a shield on one side and grasped in her other hand a figure of Victory with outspread wings.

The Athenians were critical and inclined to be irritable. They could not bear to see anyone remain in power for a long time without making him feel how uncertain his position really was. Since they did not dare to attack Pericles himself, some ill-natured people slandered Phidias, his friend, who was in charge of all the reconstruction of the city and of the Acropolis, and held a position which many of them would have liked to have occupied. He was accused of having kept for himself a portion of the precious metals which the treasury had handed to him when he was making the statue of the goddess Athena. This manœuvre only made Phidias smile. Having foreseen that such slanderous accusations might be made against him, he had fixed all the precious metals on the statue in such a way that it was possible to remove them without injuring his work of art. This was done, the gold and silver and ivory were weighed and, as nothing was missing, the sculptor was proved innocent.

Some time afterwards, people began to say that the buildings on the Acropolis were costing the government a great deal.

"Of course, these temples are splendid," the critics said, "and of course the goddess will be delighted, but the treasury is empty and the taxes are far too high. It isn't Pericles who is paying for all that!"

Pericles was soon told about these ill-natured rumours. He went to the assembly of the citizens which was held on a hill called the Pnyx, opposite the Acropolis; from there could be seen rising on that hallowed mount the new monuments with their marbles, their painted sculptures and their dazzling statues. He climbed on to the tribune, or speaker's dais—a simple flagstone rising up out of the chalky soil.

"Look!" he said to the people, "look at these splendid buildings. One day they will be the glory of our city and strangers will cross the seas to admire them, declaring on their return: 'The sons of Athens have built for their goddess the most splendid temples in the whole world.'"

"They cost far too much," cried the crowd. Pericles leant forward on the tribune, "O citizens of Athens, do you really believe that the treasury has paid out too much money?"

"Too much, too much," they cried.

"Well, my friends, they will cost you nothing, not a talent, not a drachma will be taken out of the Treasury for this purpose, and all that has been already paid out to the workmen and to the contractors will be refunded."

"And by whom?"

"By me."

An astonished silence greeted these words.

"By me," continued the orator, "but on the façades of these buildings will be engraved the following words: 'Pericles son of Xanthippus has had these temples built at his expense and dedicated them to the gods.'"

A storm of shouting interrupted Pericles. Seized with admiration for the splendour of this gesture, or refusing to let the speaker have the glory of such an enterprise, the people yelled: "Take what you like, empty the treasury, you have our trust. May the gods preserve you for our continued affection!"

But the gods do not always favour those who have honoured them so lavishly. Intoxicated by his successes and by the glory and renown of Athens, Pericles passed a law which inflicted great hardship on the dependent city of Megara.

Now Sparta, the political rival of Athens, was allied to all the other towns of the Peloponnesus and this moment seemed to provide an opportunity to injure her enemy. Polyarces, the Spartan ambassador asked for an audience with the council of Athens and demanded that the decree against the people of Megara should be withdrawn.

"It is against our laws," said Pericles, "to withdraw a decree once it has been voted for by the people."

"Do not withdraw it," replied the Spartan, smiling, "all you have to do is to modify it."

But this cunning advice was not followed. The gods, they say, blind those whom they wish to destroy. Pericles persisted; and the Spartans invaded Attica, cutting down the olive trees, tearing up the vines, burning down the villages. Pericles, with a return to his former caution, refused to fight a pitched battle. Instead he ordered all the peasants to leave their farms without attempting to resist and to take refuge in Athens so as to be under the protection of the ramparts.

The Athenian fleet left Piraeus to carry fire and destruction to the cities of the Peloponnesus.

The evacuation with all its miseries began. Day by day, the pitiful procession of refugees flowed in—urging on their cattle, dragging their families and household goods towards the city; day after day, these poor frightened people passed through the gates, hungry and heartbroken, seeking lodging with relatives or friends; when all the houses were full, they sheltered in the public buildings, in the temples and even at the feet of the gods.

The unbearable heat of summer was upon them; water began to be scarce; the people, crowded into every available space, were suffocating.

Soon a terrible rumour spread through the city: the plague! Far more dangerous than the Spartan soldiers, this scourge soon reduced the population of Athens by half. It spread like wildfire. Ten patients—a hundred patients, a thousand patients—they lay on beds of purple and fine linen, or on wretched bunks, with swollen throats and festering skin. They begged for water or for the medical attention which was not available. They filled up the houses, the courtyards, the streets and the squares; the corpses which they did not dare to burn or to bury—because people were afraid to touch them—now brought infection to the last of the healthy citizens. Even the animals—the dogs and the cattle brought in from the fields—perished by thousands. A few convalescents looked at each other with surprise, scarcely realising that they had survived.

The plague spread to the house of Pericles. His eldest son died, then his sister and, afterwards, his most faithful servants—the friends whom he consulted when he was in difficulties. Conscious that he had to set a good example, Pericles tried to remain calm, to face up to the misfortunes of his private life and to the grave responsibilities of his public office. One son alone remained to him. Alas! This young man was stricken too and succumbed. On the day when he had to place the funeral wreath of the dead on the brow of his son, the father faltered. Seized with sudden weakness for the first time in his life, he broke down and wept bitterly. Then, hiding his face in his cloak, he shut himself up in his house and refused to appear in public.

In the month of September 429 B.C. he fell ill in his turn. The illness wore him down persistently for many days.

Soon he was near to death. Around his bed, with their eyes full of tears, his friends recalled the wonders he had performed: "He was victorious in nine battles," said one.

"He gained all hearts by his eloquence," said another, and so on.

The dying statesman opened his eyes. "My friends, these are not my greatest claims to glory. You must say rather that I have never been the cause of sorrow to any of my fellow-citizens."

Scarcely had he pronounced these words, when he died.

After the death of Pericles, the glory of Athens faded.

17

The Handsomest but not the Best

ALCIBIADES was certainly the handsomest of the Athenians in the age of Pericles. The gods, as they used to say, had smiled on this young man from the day of his birth. Belonging to one of the noblest families in Athens, rich and free to live a life of pleasure, he was nevertheless as gifted intellectually as he was physically. He was an adept in all the arts and sciences of his day, but he resolutely refused to learn to play the flute.

"People who learn to play the flute," he used to say, "deform their faces so much that they are scarcely recognisable, even by their best friends. What is more, when you have the instrument in your mouth, you can't talk, and that's a disaster for any Athenian.

"That sort of thing is all right for the rustic Boeotians who are so silly that they can scarcely string two words together, but certainly not for us. We must imitate

Athena and Apollo, for the goddess threw away a flute which was given to her because it distorted her features, and the god flayed the satyr Marsyas who was expert in playing that instrument."

On the other hand, Alcibiades liked to strum on his lyre and use it to accompany his singing.

But with all his grace and intelligence, this handsomest of Athenians was not popular. He had a really strange character for he was conceited, eccentric and insolent. He was never consistent, often contradicting the things he had said in the past so that it was quite impossible to take him seriously. In Sparta, for instance, he was believed to have all the virtues of a Spartan, to be tireless, austere, courageous and tough; in Ionia he set the Ionians an example of idleness and luxury.

He often amused himself by posing as an idle young man who only thought of leading a life of pleasure. Those who were taken in by this attitude must have been real simpletons. Sooner or later, they were made to realise that this elegant trifling concealed a will of iron and inordinate pride. Even in his childhood, his behaviour had made a great impression. One day when he was playing at knuckle-bones in the street with some of his friends (for rich children were not above playing on the pavements of Athens), a heavily loaded cart drove up.

"Stop! Stop!"

The man did not even hear; he urged on his horse over the place where the boys were playing. They all scattered quickly and stood aside with their backs to the walls, but little Alcibiades was so furious that he threw himself under the wheels of the cart rather than give way.

"Now drive on," he cried to the carter.

The latter quickly reined in his horses and the boy got up, rather bruised but very pleased to have had his way.

No less odd was the respect and affection which Alcibiades had for his tutor Socrates. Socrates was not at all like his pupil. He also achieved great fame and with far more reason than Alcibiades, for he was a wise man, one of those people whom we have been led by the Greeks to call philosophers. He taught men to think clearly, to choose the best things in life and to distinguish the false from the true. Socrates was old, ugly and poor; his pupils would have paid anything he liked for his lessons, but he refused both money and honours, for he believed that the greatest glory lies in wisdom.

Although the old master was severe and critical he had a weakness for Alcibiades. He thought that wealth, noble birth and flattery would eventually lead the young man astray, and that he would come to a foolish end without realising what he might have achieved. Ugly and poor as he himself was, the old man pitied the splendid Alcibiades who, on the other hand, had a real veneration for Socrates.

"It is obvious," he used to say, "that it is the gods who inspired Socrates to teach the young men of our city."

Thus there grew up a real friendship between these two Athenians who were so different in every way. Haughty and difficult with everybody else, Alcibiades always became modest and tractable when he was with Socrates. During a military campaign, he attached himself to his master, sharing his tent, refusing to leave him and behaving with the greatest bravery. Once, when

Alcibiades was wounded, Socrates interposed his own body to protect the younger man from the attacks of the enemy. Another time, whilst Socrates was retreating on foot in the course of a battle, Alcibiades refused to ride away and leave his master in the lurch.

Alcibiades loved to attract attention by his extravagant and sometimes insolent behaviour. Once, during a banquet, when he had drunk rather too much, he took a bet that he would strike the face of one of the most distinguished citizens of Athens—an old man called Hipponicus, who was as wealthy as he was respected. On the next day, in the square, Alcibiades went up to Hipponicus, slapped his face and then disappeared.

Fortunately, the young man was intelligent enough to realise that this behaviour disgraced him far more than it affected his victim. The better side of his nature came to the fore and he determined to make amends for this foolish act. At dawn, the very next morning, he went to the house of Hipponicus; a surprised slave opened the door, and Alcibiades went straight to the master of the house, cast his cloak and his tunic at his feet and stripped like a slave.

He folded his arms, and said to Hipponicus: "Hipponicus, I place myself in your hands. Do with me what you like: to make up for my rudeness, I am prepared to undergo any punishment you like."

Hipponicus displayed his noble character to the full; he refused to avenge himself on the young man and forgave him everything.

There is another story which the Athenians liked to tell about Alcibiades:

Alcibiades had bought a very fine dog for a very high

price; in fact, he had paid seven thousand drachma for it. Wherever he went, he was accompanied by this dog, whose appearance became very familiar to everyone in Athens. In particular, the dog's tail—it was thick and very bushy—aroused general admiration and it was the main reason for the high price Alcibiades had paid.

Everybody was most surprised when the dog suddenly appeared in town without its tail. People were terribly indignant! "The poor creature! Unfortunate Alcibiades! Who can the scoundrel be who has mutilated this splendid dog, and done such a dirty trick to his master?"

The cobblers and the dyers of the Agora stood on their doorsteps to watch Alcibiades pass by with his hound. There was a tremendous amount of gossip and soon, throughout the whole city, people were saying, "Someone has cut off the tail of Alcibiades' dog. Who can possibly have done it?"

It was quite another story when the truth was learnt. Alcibiades had done it himself.

"What an odd thing to do," said the gossips, "and how he shows off! He wants everybody to see that seven thousand drachma mean absolutely nothing to him! Or perhaps he has got tired of the dog. He cut off his tail so that nobody else should buy it . . ." and so on. . . .

Rather upset by all this talk, some friends told Alcibiades what people were saying about him: "You'd better look out Alcibiades, you should at least keep your dog at home, for all this gossip will do you a great deal of harm."

The young man burst out laughing. "So people are talking about my dog, are they. They say that I am cruel and rather stupid, don't they? Everyone wants to know why I've wasted so much money and mutilated such a fine animal. Well, that is exactly what I want! I hope they go on like that. Nothing will stop the Athenians from gossiping, for they are incapable of thinking of serious matters, incapable of paying full attention to the affairs of state. They simply have to tear each other to bits . . . how one man made his fortune, how another has spent everything he has got, and so on. Well I've given them something to talk about! Let them get all the fun they can out of my dog. In the meantime, they won't gossip about my household, my wife or anything else that is close to my heart."

Unfortunately, the Athenians allowed themselves to be led astray by this man who despised them. One day when he was walking across the square, he saw poor people lined up, waiting for a free distribution of wheat. Immediately, he sent his slave back to get some money and, adding his charity to the charity of the state, he threw handfuls of coins into the crowd, with the result that shortly afterwards he was elected to high power.

In the long run, the people of Athens had no reason to be pleased with their choice. Alcibiades got involved in the terrible Peloponnesian war which had begun so badly with the epidemic of plague in Athens and the death of Pericles. He showed no more common sense in handling the interests of the nation than in dealing with his own private affairs. He was many times victorious, many times defeated, but dishonoured himself by committing high treason. Eventually, he was forced to leave the country and died miserably in exile.

18

The End of a Splendid Dream

T the beginning of August in the year 415 B.C., the entire population of Athens flocked to the port of Piraeus, nearly seven miles from the centre of the city. For the past six years there had been a truce in the bitter Peloponnesian War against the Spartans.

Why then were these thousands of heavily armed footsoldiers, or hoplites, embarking? Why these splendid triremes straight from the shipyards and covered with emblems? Had the truce come to an end?

Not yet. This fleet was sailing to attack Syracuse—the largest town in Sicily, colonised centuries before by Greeks from Corinth. Syracuse had attacked Segesta. This nearby city, also inhabited by people of Greek stock, had appealed to the Athenians for help.

Inflamed by the eloquence of Alcibiades, who was always ready with rash plans and promises, the Athenians had voted to go to the help of their allies. Actually, although the young men were ready to rush into this adventure, their elders tended to be more cautious, hoping that long years of peace would allow their city to recover from the damage done by the war against Sparta. How on earth could anyone tell what would happen?

Why should the old people have their way?

The ships decked with flags and flowers, glided gracefully out into the open sea, bearing with them the fate of Athens. With their youthful ardour, their splendid new fleet and their great naval tradition, how could anything stop the Athenians from being victorious? Then, too, they were led by the bold Alcibiades who was as handsome as a god and as courageous as one of the heroes of Antiquity.

Fifteen months passed. The setting sun was tinging the rooftops of Syracuse with its golden light and turning the sea into a sheet of flame. Inland, the violet of the mountains was deepening to indigo and the stars were about to shine in the clear southern sky. In the waters of the bay, there was nothing but confusion, torn masses of wreckage and the bodies of men killed in battle. The Athenian fleet, blockaded in the Bay of Syracuse, had tried to force a passage through the ranks of the enemy galleys. In spite of the desperate courage of their crews, the Athenians had been defeated.

Little by little, they had been driven back towards the shore. All they could attempt was to sink or burn the remains of this splendid fleet which had been their pride and their supreme hope. All day long, the hot, misty air had echoed with the clash of ship against ship and with the shouts of orders given in hoarse tones. Now, in the twilight, the hubbub was gradually dying down as the darkness thickened.

The Athenian crews, abandoning their ships, took refuge in the camp of the land forces which had been vainly besieging Syracuse for the past fifteen months. There was nothing but disorder, confusion, lamentation and despair. None of them could think of eating or of sleeping; all of them felt that they were on the brink of a national disaster and that almost inevitable death faced them.

In the midst of this turmoil, the Athenian generals Demosthenes (not the orator) and Nicias, forgetting the tenets of their religion and their national traditions, had not remembered to ask permission from the enemy to collect and bury the dead, even though such a course was usual.

What had happened then since that day when the splendid fleet had left Piraeus? Alcibiades had turned traitor. To his lasting shame, he had gone to the aid of the enemies of his country.

Nevertheless, his colleague Nicias had continued to direct operations. Syracuse had been besieged for the past fifteen months; it seemed as if the great Sicilian city was bound to fall into the hands of the Athenians. At the last minute it had been saved, although closely beleaguered by land and sea.

The help had come when the Spartan general Gylippus arrived with a fleet to rescue the besieged.

Little by little, Nicias found himself in an increasingly difficult situation, in spite of the efforts made by Demosthenes who was in command of the navy. The Athenian fleet had tried to break the blockade, but it had been completely defeated. Were the land forces to suffer the same fate?

At headquarters some attempt was made to face the situation calmly.

On his way to Nicias' tent, Demosthenes had to climb over the bodies heaped up in the darkness. Were they dead, wounded or sleeping? Nobody moved and he paid no attention to muttered curses or breaches of discipline. Around a meagre fire, a group of soldiers and sailors were cooking some food. Blood, sweat or tears flowed down their faces; one had a bandage round his leg. Not far away, a wounded man was pleading for water in a quavering voice. Such sad spectacles are only too frequent after a battle, but now there was an atmosphere of despair, brought on by defeat and the disorder of an army which has no hope of escape even by a display of outstanding courage.

Nicias came forward to welcome his colleague. He was a man of about sixty, sickly, rather timid, grey-faced and with bowed shoulders. He was said to be rich. In any case, he was an able statesman and a sound officer; he was one of those people of whom, in other circumstances, one might have said: "He is a good general who really knows his job." But fortune does not favour the old, especially if they are old in mind, timid and lacking in enterprise. In addition, Nicias was unlucky—the worst fault of all in a military commander.

"All is lost!" he murmured, coming forward.

"Come Nicias," replied Demosthenes quickly, "I have just counted the remaining ships fit for combat. We have sixty in all, whilst the Syracusans have only fifty. Let us try our luck again tomorrow."

Demosthenes had persuaded Nicias to come round to his way of thinking. There was a peal of trumpets; the crews were ordered to re-embark and prepare for action.

Alas! Cries of rebellion and hatred rose up on all sides. Convinced that they were being sent out to be slaughtered, the sailors refused to obey the order.

In the meantime, there were celebrations in Syracuse and the elders of the town were in council. From all sides came the sound of music and of cheering; everybody was filled with the enthusiasm of victory. Moreover, it was the Feast of Hercules and many a butt of wine had been emptied to toast the godly hero.

However, at least one person was not at all happy about what was happening, and that was Hermokrates, the Syracusan general. He pursed his lips and muttered to himself in dismay: "My men are drunk, it is quite impossible to prevent these accursed Athenians from getting away tonight. If he wished, Demosthenes could reorganise his army and penetrate to the heart of Sicily where he has allies, and he could re-equip his forces at leisure." After having pondered over this some time, he summoned a few reliable and intelligent men in order to send them out on a special mission.

An hour later, just as Nicias and Demosthenes were about to strike camp, they received a secret message from a Syracusan soldier. In return for a large sum of money, he told them that all roads were being occupied by the forces of his countrymen. "Do not leave tonight, but wait until tomorrow," he added.

The Athenian generals changed their plans; they

ordered their men to pile arms and to encamp for the night. They did not suspect for a single moment that they had been taken in by false information sent by the orders of Hermokrates himself. The Syracusan general intended to spend the whole of the next day blocking the roads, occupying bridges and fords, without the knowledge of the over-confident Nicias who would lose his last chance of escape.

Two days after the battle, forty thousand Athenian soldiers left the camp and set out for Catania, as full of despair as if they were leaving their own homes for ever. It was absolutely heartrending to listen to the groans and supplications of the wounded and of the sick who were being left behind.

"For heaven's sake, take me," they cried to their friends, "see I can still walk a little. . . . Don't leave me to the mercy of the Syracusans. They will cut off our hands. They will bury us alive. . . ."

With a great effort, the fittest among them tried to get up to join their comrades. Most of them were too weak and they had to be abandoned to their fate. On looking at the dead, the Athenians were overcome with sorrow at the thought of leaving their friends and relatives condemned to lose their immortality, since they would not receive proper burial. On the top of all this, even those who were unscathed by the battle were at a great disadvantage; there was a shortage of food and, as the slaves had deserted, the hoplites were obliged to carry their own baggage as well as their weapons, so that they suffered cruelly from fatigue and as a result of the heat.

As Nicias had inspired the troops with a little courage by his oratory, they were better organised; they fell back into their ranks and the day passed without any disturbance other than an occasional skirmish with the enemy.

The lack of water afflicted the Athenians cruelly in the burning sun; they would have liked to scatter over the plain in search of springs and wells, but the Syracusans barred their way.

Despite the great efforts made by the Athenians to break through, they could not overcome the resistance of the enemy. Then, to make matters worse, there was a terrible thunderstorm and the rain began to fall in torrents.

"The gods themselves are against us," thought the soldiers in their despair.

During the night, Nicias and Demosthenes attempted to outwit their enemies. Great fires were lit so as to give the impression that they were encamping permanently; then they mustered their forces and set off in an unexpected direction, which had been left unguarded by the Syracusans.

Nicias led the vanguard, whilst Demosthenes was in command of the rearguard—obviously the most dangerous post in a retreating army. In the darkness, disorder spread once more in the ranks and delayed the advance of the army, nevertheless they reached the seashore and then they came to the mouth of a river whose course they followed.

The next morning, the Syracusans caught up with Demosthenes. He tried to draw up his forces in battle order, but his tired troops moved too slowly and they were forced up against a wall surrounding an olive grove. Struck down from a distance by missiles of all sorts, overcome by thirst, heat and wounds, the soldiers of the rear-guard surrendered, handed over their weapons and all the money they possessed and were led off as prisoners to Syracuse.

Nicias had foolishly outdistanced his colleague. He did not realise what had happened until he was told of the surrender by the Syracusans on the next day. In his despair, he was prepared to discuss terms, but the conditions laid down by Gylippus were so harsh that, in the end, he refused to accept them.

When night fell once more, Nicias ordered his troops to muster and attempt escape. Scarcely had the Athenians seized their weapons than they heard the Spartans singing a war-song, to show that their manœuvre had been discovered.

At dawn, the unfortunate Athenians, at the end of their tether, were being harassed by the enemy as they made their way with the greatest difficulty to the bank of a little river called the Asinarus.

It was there that the last scene of the great tragedy was to be unfolded. The river had to be crossed, but the soldiers cared more about quenching their thirst than about their safety. They rushed into the water, tripped each other up, fell on the top of each other, and presented the easiest of targets to the enemy missiles. The Syracusans advanced towards the river whose steep banks prevented the victims from getting away quickly.

The slaughter was so terrible that Nicias surrendered simply on condition that the massacre should cease. And so, soon after, the survivors were led into Syracuse as prisoners, to rejoin the forces of Demosthenes which had been captured the day before.

In spite of the opposition of the Spartans and of their general, Gylippus, the Syracusans were so angered that they executed Demosthenes and Nicias. As for the remaining Athenian prisoners, they were taken down to the Latomiae—deep quarries which had been excavated in order to extract the stone for the construction of Syracuse.

It was quite impossible for the unfortunate Athenians to escape from these huge pits. Baked by the sun or drenched by the rain, short of food and of water, seven thousand Athenians endured the most terrible suffering for seventy days. The few who survived were sold as slaves.

Thus, the expedition to Sicily ended in disgrace and suffering. Nevertheless, Athens recovered from this disaster and, such was the vitality of this wonderful city, it looked for a while as if her good fortune would return, for the Athenians then threatened the security of Sparta once more. However, they were decisively beaten by the Spartans in the year 405 B.C. and the decline continued.

If you visit the Latomiae to-day you will find a completely different scene. The crickets fill the air with their musical shrilling, the scent of flowers is intoxicating and the oleanders sway in the wind. Everything is radiant and the atmosphere is gay and happy, for time effaces the memory of the greatest of suffering and Nature embellishes the places which have been devastated and spoiled by man.

19

The Death of a Wise Man

LOFTY hills half hid the rising sun; the town itself was still plunged in the darkness of night. The fresh wind of dawn had begun to blow and the carrion crows had started to wheel in the sky where the stars were fading. It was not an unusually early hour for Athens. The heat of the day is intense in Athens still to-day, and, as the streets quickly become unbearably warm when the sun is high, the Athenians rise early. The tradesmen unhook the shutters from their shopfronts, and the porters unbolt the great doors of the houses or cheerfully shout to each other across the street.

But to return to the days of Antiquity: who were these people standing in front of a low door? There were three or four silent men; each had his face veiled in a fold of his cloak. Others arrived, walking up the steep street. They were out of breath from the climb and they greeted each other sadly.

"Can it be true, Phaedon," murmured young Crito.

"Are you certain that the sacred trireme has returned from Delos?"

"Alas, it is only too true. When we came out of the prison yesterday evening, the galley had just been rowed into the port."

"Is there no hope of a fresh respite?"

"Don't be foolish, Crito! You know very well that our master has already had his sentence postponed for a long spell; it was lucky that the sacred galley had left on its pilgrimage to Delos the day before sentence was pronounced. The judges had to obey the law: no prisoner must be executed before the return of the ship. The judges would certainly have been glad to put him to death at once, this well-beloved master of ours, but the gods protected Socrates, for the priest of Apollo had already placed a wreath on the prow of the ship and the pilgrimage had started. That's why we have had the joy of being able to spend another thirty days with Socrates. The time is up now. We may as well resign ourselves, Crito, for I don't even know if our master himself wants a second postponement of his sentence."

This was the calm, sad way in which the friends of Socrates talked at the gate of the prison a few hours before his death. Though their sorrow was great, it was softened by the divine serenity that their master had been able to inspire in them up to this moment. He was not like the other condemned men who were awakening for the last time in the prison of Athens; those who loved him felt that they ought to mourn him as a hero who had reached the supreme moment of his life.

For the past seventy years—a most dramatic and brilliant period in the history of the city—nobody had been better known and better loved than the wise Socrates. Socrates had neither wealth, military genius, statesmanship nor artistic talents. He was poor and of humble birth; his father was a sculptor of cheap statues and his mother was a midwife. His ugliness was proverbial, for he had a flat nose, thick lips and prominent eyes, so that he looked like a woodland satyr.

In spite of his slender means, Socrates gave up his time to the study of science, but he quickly came to the conclusion that the study of man was more interesting still. So the latter part of his life was devoted to the self-imposed task of teaching, to the exclusion of all other business—public or private—and without any thought of making money. On seeing that he was always cheerful, in spite of his poverty and his humble condition, and hearing him talk so clearly and so interestingly about everything, a number of Athenians followed him, and beseeched him to accept them as pupils and as friends.

Socrates taught everywhere—in public places, in the parks, whilst dining with friends or walking along the banks of the Ilyssus, the little river which flowed through the fields near Athens surrounded by shady groves and glades full of flowers.

No one could be less like an ordinary schoolmaster than this philosopher who gossiped rather than taught, joking with some, mocking others, disdaining both money and honours.

Of course, Socrates was not liked by everybody, certainly not by those whose ridiculous tricks or vices he exposed. When Athens had lost the Peloponnesian War and people accused each other bitterly of having caused this disaster, some particularly ill-natured people wished to get rid of Socrates. He was put on trial and accused of contempt of the gods, for the citizens believed that the gods would avenge themselves on Athens where they had been bodly defied.

Socrates was seventy years old; this was a great age at a time when the span of life was shorter than it is to-day. He sincerely thought that after his death he would find himself in a far better world. He scarcely took the trouble to defend himself, angered the judges, and allowed himself to be condemned to death to the great despair of his friends.

One morning, Crito came to see him, radiant with joy, saying: "Socrates, everything is ready for your flight; all that we need is your consent. I have bribed the jailors, you can escape in disguise; within a few days, you will be in Thessaly, staying with friends of mine who will be only too pleased to welcome you."

"Think this over, Crito," said Socrates "and see if you don't change your mind."

Gently he explained his ideas: "I have always professed to respect the laws. Should I now break them simply because they do not suit my convenience? If I were on the point of escaping, I should see these laws rise up in front of me and accuse me: 'What are you about to do, Socrates? Aren't you trying to destroy both the laws and the state? Do you think that a town can survive when the decrees which are made have no force, when anybody who wishes to do so can treat them as if they didn't exist? You have loved this town, Socrates, you have profited by its sound administration. Are you prepared to-day to show lack of respect for the laws which have protected you in the past? Where will you go

Socrates? In your new home will you teach the virtues and the justice which you have despised here? Better lose your life and endure an unjust condemnation with bravery, return good for evil, and display your virtue to those who have suspected it'."

Whilst Socrates spoke these noble words, with the calmness of wisdom, Crito felt his hopes vanish. How could he persuade Socrates to prefer life to a clear conscience.

"Speak now, Crito," said Socrates; "if you think you can convince me, speak on."

"No Socrates," he replied sadly, "I have nothing to say to you."

Thus Socrates had refused to escape from the sentence of death. Now the time had come: the last day of his life was dawning. The jailor opened the door.

"Be patient for a moment, my friends," he said in a low voice "I must free Socrates from his chains for this is the day of his execution."

Xanthippe, the wife of the philosopher, was sitting by his side: on her knees sat her newborn child. She was weeping.

"Come, Crito," said Socrates, "take Xanthippe home; it will be better for her."

When she had gone, he began to rub his legs where the chain had chafed them, saying: "See, my friends, how pleasure and pain go together. I was suffering because of this chain and now that I am freed from it, I feel better."

On seeing him so calm and peaceful, his friends felt their own sorrow and pain disappear. When he began to talk to them just as calmly as in the past, it seemed that nothing had changed. They discoursed together all day, of life and especially of death, of the great hopes that the philosopher had of a far better world.

"It is only when my soul shall be delivered from my body," he said, "that it will find true happiness. Would it not be ridiculous for a man who has spent his life despising his body, to be filled with sorrow when he is on the point of getting rid of it."

"It is obvious," he added, "that our soul does not die when it passes over into the Unknown; it only takes with it the vestiges of the good and the evil that we have done. Let us strive therefore to be kindly, courageous and just. Those who have despised pleasures and vanities in their lifetime can be confident about the fate of their souls. As for me, my destiny is settled, my time has come."

"How do you wish us to bury you?" asked his friends.

The philosopher smiled.

"Do what you like, my friends. What can it matter to me; it is not I, but my body which you are going to display, burn and bury. As for me, I am departing to the land of the happy."

At that moment, the jailor appeared.

"Socrates," said he, "I know that I have nothing to reproach you with and that you will not be angry with me. You are the gentlest and the best of those whom I have seen in this place. You know what I have to tell you. You must face your fate as best you can."

And, starting to weep, he went away.

"That," said Socrates, "is an excellent fellow. During the whole of my stay here, he has often kept me company; see how moved he is. Come, let them bring the poison."

It was the custom in Athens to execute the condemned by making them drink hemlock.

Soon the jailor returned bringing a cup, full to the brim.

"Well, my friend," said Socrates calmly, "you, who know all about these things, tell me what to do."

"Nothing at all," replied the other, "except to walk about a little after having drunk, until your legs become heavy; then you must lie down."

The old man took the cup and drained it without a tremor. His friends could not refrain from weeping and lamenting on seeing this, but he said: "What is the matter with you? What was the good of sending away the women if you weep in their place? Should not our end be reached serenly? Be calm, be strong. . . ."

Soon Socrates veiled his face, then baring it once more, he said: "Crito, I owe Aesculapius a cock, see that it is given to him."

These were his last words.

Such was the end of Socrates, one of the wisest and best men of all time.

20

How to become an Orator

AWYERS were always busy in Athens, for the Athenians loved to sue each other. This was partly because they were quarrelsome but also because they appreciated great eloquence. However, their law courts were organised in a very curious way.

It was not a judge who pronounced the sentences but a jury composed of two hundred, five hundred, or even fifteen hundred jurymen selected from among the Heliastes—those six thousand citizens chosen by lot each year for this purpose.

Athenians were very proud to be appointed to this body, and were ready to enjoy the power and dignity conferred on them by the white or black pebble which they had to put into the ballot box.

The interest of the people was greatest when an official who could not balance his accounts, an ambassador who

The old man took the cup

had not looked after the interests of the state, or a general whose carelessness had lost a battle appeared before the magistrates. In addition, this gave the lawyers good opportunity to exercise their talent.

The inflexible rule was that the parties to the disputes had to do their own pleading. But they were allowed to have their speeches prepared for them by lawyers as long as they delivered them themselves.

So the legal profession flourished in Athens; fees varied enormously—beginners charged very little, but brilliant and experienced men had to be highly paid. Besides this, the law was a profession which afforded an ambitious man plenty of scope: when some of these lawyers took to politics they were able to make use of the eloquence they had acquired as lawyers.

Day had scarcely dawned. Two elderly men were making their way along one of the winding streets of Athens.

"Hurry up, my friend!" said the older of the two. "The sun is already rising above the crest of the Acropolis and most of the seats in court will be occupied by the time we get there."

"You take your job very seriously," replied the other. "You are just like one of those fellows who wait outside the courts all night to be sure of getting a good seat."

"I don't go as far as that, but I am very much interested in the case which is being tried to-day, although I don't know the young man who is pleading."

"Well," replied the other, "you don't know him but you must have known his father, Demosthenes, who was nicknamed the "Polisher" because he spent all his time burnishing the shields and the swords made in his arms factory. He had some special trick to put a wonderful shine on everything he touched; that was supposed to be the secret of his success.

"Unfortunately, the poor man had a heart attack, and his widow, his seven-year-old son and his little girl of five were looked after by three guardians. Old Demosthenes had made a will and a very carefully drawn up will too; he had taken every precaution to see that his family was provided for. But precautions are useless when a rather silly woman and her two children are in the hands of three rascals."

"I quite agree with you," said the younger man. "So I suppose that to-day the young Demosthenes is suing his three guardians."

"Not exactly, only one of them, a man called Aphobos. Young Demosthenes is twenty-one years old now, and he is energetic and intelligent. It is true that his education was neglected because of the wickedness of his guardians, but he made up for it by working hard on his own, and I think that his mother did help him a little, though they were very hard up. They had to eat salt fish instead of meat, and porridge on most days of the week. Then, on top of it all, the young fellow is in very poor health."

Still talking, the two men reached the Agora and went into the enclosure reserved for the tribunal.

After the sacrifice and a prayer, a herald proclaimed a list of the cases due to be tried and then the first pleader rose to his feet. It was Demosthenes, a rather unattractive young man, thin and round-shouldered with his head closely shaved. He was terribly pale and the members of the jury looked with pity at this young man who was trembling with emotion and had the utmost difficulty in controlling himself.

"If Aphobos had behaved like an honest man, or allowed our friends to settle matters for him, there would have been no trial and no waste of time to-day."

These first words were uttered with the greatest of difficulty. He hesitated, he repeated himself and seemed to have a very bad stammer. However, little by little, he succeeded in controlling himself. The judges, who appreciated great eloquence, looked highly critical. Badly composed and badly uttered, this pleading would have been useless in any other case, but it was obvious that Aphobos had behaved very wrongly.

"This young Demosthenes is really plucky, and his guardian is a thorough scoundrel," murmured one of the jurymen to his neighbour. "He will certainly win his case, but he won't make his fortune as a public speaker. The best thing he can do is to work in his father's factory and avoid making speeches."

Twenty-five years have passed since this story began. It is evening. Suddenly a horseman gallops into the Agora. He is grey with dust and his mount is covered with foam. He is a messenger! The man reins in his horse in front of the door of the round building, called the Tholos. Here live the fifty representatives entrusted by the assembly to watch over the affairs of state. The newcomer rushes in and shuts the door behind him. Immediately a crowd gathers round the horse which is still steaming and trembling with the strain of the journey.

"Where do you think he comes from?"

"He must have done at least thirty miles to be in that condition."

"I wonder what can have happened."

"It must be those Macedonians again."

For the past twenty years the Athenians had been engaged in a cold war in which they were bound to be the losers. Philip, king of Macedonia, an ambitious, turbulent but likable monarch, realised that he would never dominate Greece as long as Athens was independent. He frequently attacked the Athenians, sometimes victoriously, but never with complete success, and yet the time seemed to have come for a decisive battle.

Numerous allies had joined the Athenians, for each of the city-states had realised that it was to their interest to unite rather than to let themselves be destroyed piecemeal. Thebes was still hesitating; powerful Thebes, not far from Athens; the town which was the strongest of all from the military point of view. But the people of Thebes were uncertain, and no one knew whether they would range themselves with King Philip or with the other Greek cities.

People in the square wanted to know what had happened. As they waited outside the closed building, the minutes passed with agonising slowness. At last the door was opened, the president appeared. Raising his hand for silence, he spoke in a trembling voice:

"Citizens of Athens, Elateia is taken!"

Everyone in the crowd shouted out in dismay: "Elateia taken; and it's only three days' journey away!"

"Tell us what happened?"

The Macedonians had attacked the town without warning. As the inhabitants were unprepared, their town was captured without any difficulty.

Exaggerated rumours spread round Athens like wild-fire. That evening, not a citizen stayed at home. Who could sit down to a pleasant family meal on the terrace and enjoy roast hare and olives, at such a time? Even the children stopped playing with their knuckle-bones or their terracotta dolls, for they were afraid to leave their parents. Officials came down to the Agora. They tore down the hutments of the merchants, overturned the stalls of the moneylenders, piled up the fragments of wood and lit huge fires to summon countrymen to the assembly early the next day.

Dawn came. The anxious Athenians were already crowding the terraces of the assembly.

One or two leading citizens started to address the people but were received with shouts of derision. At last, a frail-looking man slowly climbed up the steps of the tribune and was greeted with loud cheers. He stooped as he walked and his hands were tightly clasped together, whilst his cloak of finest wool left one of his shoulders uncovered.

"Citizens of Athens," he said in a ringing voice, in tones so mellow that they aroused the sympathy of every listener.

A tremor of excitement and joy ran through the crowd. "There he is! Listen—listen carefully! We can yet be saved."

He explained how the capture of Elateia, which seemed so harmful to the city of Athens, might, on the contrary, prove helpful. Elateia is nearer to Thebes than to Athens. Would the Boeotians allow themselves to be threatened in this way? Surely they would take up arms against the king of Macedonia.

As he continued his speech, the orator's own enthusiasm swept through the crowd like a gust of wind. His musical voice and clear utterance, together with his moving gestures, magnified the effects of his eloquent words. Sometimes, it almost seemed as if he were speaking in verse. At the end of his speech the orator was greeted with frenzied cheers. The Athenians who had been so dejected a short while ago were filled with hope once more.

"We must mobilise our forces," he concluded, "and we must send out embassies. As for me, I am getting old but the Athenians will admit that I have been of some service to my country. The moment has come when still more is expected of me. I shall go as ambassador to Thebes. May the gods be with me in all my efforts."

Philip was already conquered by the eloquence of Demosthenes.

PART FOUR

STORIES OF ALEXANDER THE GREAT

A Torch to Burn the whole of Asia

NE often sees in history books, pictures of a young man with curly hair and regular features. His head is usually inclined a little to one side. At first glance, you might think it was a god, someone like Apollo, Hermes or Dionysus. Indeed, from the point of view of the people of the Ancient World, Alexander was almost a god; many great men came near to worshipping him.

"I weep," said Caesar when he was thirty-one years old, "because, at my age, Alexander had conquered the world."

What Alexander did is almost unbelievable. He was little more than a boy when he brought the immense empire of the Persians to an end and, without the help of man or compass, led a handful of Greeks from the diminutive land of Macedonia across the boundless deserts of Asia, as far as India.

Alexander's father was King Philip against whom Demosthenes expended his eloquence. A real soldier and an able statesman, he was tough and cunning too. He was also a terrible drunkard like most of the Macedonians over whom he reigned. This nation came to prominence rather late in the history of Greece. They dwelt in the thickly wooded and mountainous north. They were not very civilised, and were so brutal that they were despised by the other Greeks who looked on them as uneducated peasants. Their kings often had trouble with the undisciplined local chiefs; but, little by little, the Macedonian army improved and their way of fighting in a formation, known as a phalanx, became celebrated. By this system, groups of soldiers were trained to fight in columns, sixteen men deep. Each man was armed with a long pike so that the army appeared like an enormous and menacing hedgehog. Within the phalanx itself there were also bowmen and javelin men and the whole formation advanced at the double. The wedge-shaped Macedonian phalanx was so heavy that for many years it never failed to break through other armies and disperse greatly superior forces.

With his well-disciplined and reorganised army, Philip defeated the Athenians at Chaeroneia, and became master of all the Greek states. He treated these conquered peoples with the greatest leniency and allowed them to form into a federation.

In 349 B.C., eleven years before this battle, two strangers had arrived at Pella, the capital of Macedonia. They were dark-skinned and bearded, and they wore robes of many colours and felt caps, like the Persians. They were, indeed, two Persian lords named Artabezus and Menapos. They were governors of provinces—known as satraps in their own country—and they were ready to rebel against their king.

During their stay in Pella, a Greek child often walked with them in the palace gardens. He was fair and rather sturdy. His fine, regular features made one forget that, owing to slight weakness in one muscle, his head was tilted to one side and that one of his eyes was blue while the other was black. This was Alexander, son of Philip, and at that time he was seven years old.

He frequently talked to the Persians and asked them endless questions about their own country. He asked about the kind of weapons used in the Persian army, the names of their best regiments, the time required to go from Pella to Susa and the way of life of the Persian king and his court.

One day, after the boy had left them, the two satraps began to talk about him.

"That's a really intelligent child," said Menapos, "and he doesn't waste his time either. Have you noticed how precise and searching his questions are?"

"That's true, Menapos, and it's true also that his father takes the greatest care of him."

"Many things are said about this child," replied Menapos thoughtfully. "The night of his birth the temple at Ephesus burst into flames, and the seers immediately declared that a torch had been lit which would burn up the whole of Asia."

A great deal of trouble was taken over the education of young Alexander. When the child was thirteen years old,

King Philip sent a letter to the philosopher Aristotle asking him to become his son's tutor: "I thank the gods," he wrote, "not so much for having given me a son as because he was born in your lifetime."

On reading these words, Aristotle found it impossible to refuse such a kindly invitation. He came to Pella and remained there for three years teaching his young pupil and other Macedonians of the same age.

Now Aristotle was a great scientist as well as a philosopher and writer. He taught the young prince all that he knew about medicine, mathematics and geography, besides, of course, teaching him how to think clearly about everything. From that time, Alexander always retained great reverence for the works of Homer, reverence which had been inspired in him by his teacher.

Eight years passed and Alexander was fifteen years old. One morning, there was great shouting and agitation in the courtyard of the palace, for a countryman had offered the king an exceptional horse, a priceless animal, which he was ready to sell for sixteen talents.

However, the king could not make up his mind, for Bucephalus—this was the name of the animal—appeared to be a wild beast rather than a horse. No one could stay a moment on his back. Both gentleness and severity had been tried in vain. As soon as a rider mounted, the horse reared up and threw him to the ground.

At first, Philip was very much amused, then suddenly he grew angry: "Take away your horse," he cried to the merchant, "he is going to cripple all my horsemen. Why, your beast isn't even broken in!"

"He's all right if he's properly handled," replied the merchant who was very anxious to sell the horse. "You

Suddenly a horseman galloped into the Agora

must agree that he is a thoroughbred. Look at his shoulders, his neck, his hocks. . . ."

"What do you think about it, Alexander?" growled Philip, turning towards his son.

"I think your men are spoiling a good horse and that they don't know their job."

Philip whistled between his teeth.

"Luckily for them, you're here to teach them their trade."

"Perhaps, especially if you'll let me break in this horse."

Philip was in a very good temper. "And if you fail, how will you pay for your presumption?"

"I'll pay for the horse."

Alexander went up to Bucephalus, took him by one rein and turned his head towards the sun.

"This horse," he said, "is afraid of his own shadow."

Then he stroked the animal's neck and suddenly leapt onto his back. Alexander's knees gripped so tightly that the horse realised he had found a master and gradually calmed down. Finally, Alexander galloped off across the plain.

"He'll be thoroughly broken in when I come back," he cried. This was exactly what happened and from that time onwards Bucephalus accompanied Alexander in all his campaigns. As for the Macedonians, they were very much impressed and the prince became even more popular than before.

Some time afterwards, Alexander went with his father on a military expedition against the Scythian tribes— the Barbarians who inhabited the plain between the Carpathians and the River Don. There was some fierce fighting and Philip was wounded, but his son saved his life. Ever afterwards the king limped, and this exasperated him.

"You shouldn't complain, Father," said the young prince, "for every step you take must remind you of your own courage."

In spite of this, the king and his son did not get on very well, for Alexander was becoming jealous of his father's many victories. He used to say rather sorrowfully to his friends: "My father will leave us nothing to conquer."

But Philip was murdered in 336 B.C., so that Alexander had an early opportunity of showing what he could do.

22

The Tomb of Achilles

FTER having punished the Greeks for rebelling at the time of Philip's death, Alexander decided to prepare an immense expedition against Persia. In this way, instead of the Persians invading Greece, a Greek army was about to sweep through Asia.

Alexander announced that he was afraid of being attacked by the Persians, but this was only a pretext for declaring war. The Persian king at that time, who was called Darius like his ancestors, was not at all adventurous. His own empire kept him busy and he was very wealthy.

In the spring of 334 B.C., a Macedonian army of thirty thousand foot soldiers, and eighteen hundred horsemen set off, carrying with them rations for thirty days. Before he left, Alexander distributed all his personal belongings to those of his friends who remained in Macedonia.

"What are you keeping for yourself?" asked one of them in surprise.

"Hope," replied Alexander.

Then he left the palace in which he had spent his childhood and which he was never to see again.

The army followed in reverse the route taken by Xerxes at the time of the Wars of the Medes and Persians. The Macedonians crossed the Hellespont and landed near Troy.

The king insisted on visiting the place where the Greeks had won their first great victory a thousand years previously. He had a great sense of history and, as we know, greatly revered Homer. He always carried the works of this great poet about with him, placing them by his bedside at night together with his sword. Later on, he used to keep them in a valuable box which was looted from a Persian town. This box had been used for perfumes so that the leaves of the books became impregnated with their fragrance.

So Alexander made his way across the countryside to what was left of the city of Troy. Only a few houses remained on the little hill where Priam had been besieged for so many years. On one side, stretched the shore where Agamemnon had beached his fleet. Nearer at hand was the plain where the Greeks had encamped.

Knowing that Alexander was fond of music, one of the citizens tried to please the young king by offering him a lyre which he declared had belonged to Paris. But Paris had a rather indifferent reputation, for he had been entirely taken up with his love affairs and not prepared to risk his life in battle, so Alexander refused the present.

"I would rather have the lyre of Achilles," he said.

Indeed, he was haunted by the memory of Achilles. He felt a resemblance to this hero who, according to legend, had preferred a short but glorious life to a long existence without honour. Achilles had perished during the siege of Troy when his heel was pierced by an arrow shot by Paris, and he had been buried by his companions near the walls of the city.

Alexander piously visited the tomb, for he wished to honour Achilles in every way. He also organised Games in memory of the hero. He and his companions ran races, wrestled and competed with each other at throwing the javelin and at chariot driving, just like the heroes of the past.

Finally, Alexander climbed up to the sanctuary of Athena which had already been established at the top of the fortress in the time of Priam. He found there, hanging on a wall, an ancient suit of armour which was said to have been used in the great Trojan War. He took it, and put his own weapons in its place. From that time on, one of his squires always carried this armour, as the king considered it to be part of his inheritance from the warriors of other days.

Once, he even put it on to lead his troops in a great battle.

23

Alexander Marries the Daughter of the King of Persia

SOMBRE night was falling on the field of battle at Issos. As soon as he had seen the Macedonian king charging towards him at the head of his splendid cavalry, with his armour shining in the half light, Darius was seized with panic. His driver succeeded in making his horses wheel round in spite of all the wreckage of the battlefield. The king of the Persians was abandoning his army, though it was still fighting valiantly in spite of the prospect of certain defeat. Soon a range of mountains appeared on the horizon, and the road became difficult; Darius leapt down from his chariot, threw away his bow and his shield and even, to his shame, discarded his imperial robes. Jumping onto a horse which his equerry always led behind him, he continued his headlong flight.

Soon, deserted by the king, the Persian army gave

way; following his example, the men streamed after the fugitive monarch. Crushed in narrow gorges, they were so huddled together in their flight that one of Alexander's generals declared that he could have galloped over their bodies.

When darkness was complete, the Macedonians returned to their headquarters without having caught up with Darius. The Persian camp had fallen into the hands of the victor, and it was filled with treasures of immense value. All the women and children still remained in their tents—the Persians always brought their families with them on their military operations. The Greeks helped themselves lavishly to the gold and silver coins which had been brought to pay the enemy troops. Intoxicated with their victory, they stripped the women of their jewels, quarrelled over the booty and gave themselves up to all sorts of violence.

Nevertheless, all that had belonged to the King of Kings was reserved for Alexander. The Persian servants who had prepared a bath, a meal and a bed for Darius, now awaited the orders of their new master with oriental fatalism.

When Alexander arrived, he cast aside his weapons and leapt into the bath which had been richly perfumed. "Now," he cried laughingly, "I can wash away the sweat of battle in the bath prepared for the King of Kings."

His surgeon dressed a flesh wound in his thigh and then he put on his clothes and went into a lofty, spacious tent, hung with tapestry embroidered in gold thread with patterns of lions and birds; his feet sank into the thickest of carpets; the bed, the table, and the chairs were inlaid with gold, silver and precious stones. Well-trained slaves stood ready to serve a delicious meal which the king shared with his staff officers. As for Alexander, he was more amused than impressed by all this luxury, for he had been brought up with a most rigorous simplicity.

Nevertheless, he turned towards his friends and cried: "Darius really knew how to live like a king!"

Whilst the victors were settling down to their dinner, their ears were assailed by rending cries. The uproar came from neighbouring tents; as they did not know what was happening, the Macedonian Royal Guard came running up.

A useless precaution! The noise was made by women wailing, mourning in the traditional oriental manner. "This is because the royal princesses have been told of the death of Darius," someone said to the king.

"But Darius is not dead," explained Alexander.

"That is true, but a Persian has seen the garments and the weapons which one of your officers picked up not far from the field of battle. He came to the conclusion that the King of Kings had perished."

Alexander remained silent for a while, but the wailing and the weeping continued. "Go, Mithrenes," he said to a former governor of Sardis—a Persian who had betrayed Darius and had been admitted into his circle. "Go and tell them that they are mourning for someone who is still alive."

But Mithrenes had scarcely gone when Alexander changed his mind.

"What have I done?" said he. "I have sent them a traitor who has betrayed their country. It is quite enough to humiliate them."

And so he sent instead Leonnatos, one of his Macedonian officers, who gave the glad tidings to the mother of Darius, the king's two daughters, his wife and his son aged six.

Although the heat of battle had scarcely abated, Alexander treated these women and children with the greatest kindness. Not only did their forlorn situation appeal to his generosity, but he thought perhaps that they might prove valuable hostages in his dealings with Darius.

The next day, Alexander ordered that the bodies of all the Greek dead should be burnt, and he sent a message to the Persian princesses inviting them to attend the burial of their friends and relatives who had died in the battle.

Towards evening, Alexander decided to visit his captives. Wishing to make the most courteous approach possible, he sent a messenger to warn them of his coming. Then, fearing that he might offend these princesses who were accustomed to the seclusion of the oriental harems, he went without his armed followers, accompanied only by a close friend of his called Hephestion. This man was the same age as Alexander but much taller and of very impressive appearance. As soon as she saw the two friends come into her tent, Darius' mother took Hephestion for the king and showed him all the honours prescribed by Persian ceremonial. She knelt down and pressed her head in the dust at the feet of Alexander's lieutenant.

Horrified, the Persian servants rushed forward to warn her of her error, and Queen Sysigambis, overcome at the thought of having offended the conqueror, apologised profusely.

"My lord," she said, "I did not recognise you. I have never seen you before."

But Alexander was too intelligent to be offended by such a harmless mistake.

"Mother," he said, finding instinctively the name by which he could honour the venerable princess without humiliating himself, "you are not mistaken. Hephestion is a second Alexander."

Then, calling his officers, he told them to return to the princesses all that had been taken from them—both jewels and furniture—and to see that they were given the full honours of their rank.

Sysigambis was so delighted at this that she exclaimed: "O king, the prayers we used to offer for Darius shall now be offered for you. You called me mother and yet I should be ready to proclaim myself your servant, for just as I was able to enjoy my previous rank I must put up with my captivity to-day."

As Alexander was about to leave, he noticed a pretty child in the arms of Darius' queen. "Is that the son of Darius?" he asked. He went up to the little boy, enchanted by his grace. Immediately slipping down from his mother's arms, the child looked boldly up at the Macedonian and seized his hand.

"Well," cried Alexander, taking the small boy into his arms. "I only wish that Darius was as courageous as his son." Then he went out of the tent.

His generosity towards the women prisoners was never relaxed. When the queen died suddenly a little later, Alexander saw to it that she was buried with full royal honours.

Then, after Darius was murdered by a treacherous

satrap, Alexander took the attitude that he himself was heir to the Persian empire and he assumed full responsibility for the Persian royal family. He established Sysigambis and the other princesses in one of the palaces which had belonged to them and, on his return from India some years later, he married Stateira, the elder daughter of Darius, whilst his friend Hephestion became the husband of her younger sister.

24

Wings for the Macedonian Troops

NOW in the year 328 B.C. the Macedonians were in the province of Sogdiana—that is to say, beyond Persia in the heart of the country now called Turkestan. Alexander found himself confronted by a rock many thousand feet high. It was, in fact, a mountain in its own right. The king was furious to think that this obstacle defied him, or rather that someone on the crest of the peak was defying him.

Indeed, the Sogdian Arimazes had taken refuge in this eagle's nest with thirty thousand soldiers and plenty of money to pay them. Better still, they had enough food for two years, so that he had no reason to fear the Macedonian armies. With his own eyes, the king could see, halfway up the precipice, the mouth of a cave which served as headquarters to his enemies. A spring of clear water flowed near by. The local people declared that, although the entrance was small, there were vast grottoes within the cave which would give shelter to a whole army. It was clear, therefore, that Arimazes had no intention of coming down. Even at this distance, it was possible to see the Barbarians moving about in perfect safety, sitting round camp fires or mounting guard.

Facing Alexander there was a little path which led to the cave, but there was no question of using it, for it was narrow and very steep. Five or six determined men could defend it against an army. Naturally, the king explored every possible means of attack and made a careful survey of the surrounding countryside. Everywhere he found steep crags and precipices which made a flanking attack impossible.

For a while, Alexander was tempted to go away, to continue his journey to India, to leave Arimazes to his fate.

With his small army, the Sogdian chief could do no great harm to the Macedonians; in fact, he was not even strong enough to attack their rearguard. However, he might, in time, cut off communications with their bases in Asia Minor and in Persia and that would create great difficulties for the Macedonians. On the other hand, it seemed useless to besiege the rock, for months or even years would be required to starve out the garrison.

It was at this point, that Alexander summoned Cophes, a young Persian who had joined his forces. Cophes had been enlisted in the picked body of guards known as the Hetairoi or Companions who shared the life of the king and always took their meals with him.

"Cophes," said he, "go with a flag of truce to Arimazes and try to induce him to surrender."

Cophes set off, but the reply which he brought back made Alexander mad with rage. Arimazes, he said, had roared with laughter.

"Let your king come," was his answer, "all he has to do is to climb up this steep path! We can give him plenty of cold water to drink and we'll teach him to dance in our own rather special way."

Then as the Persian started to go away, the Sogdian had cried out: "Tell your king to get some wings for his soldiers."

Alexander was so furious that he summoned a council of war at once. Maddened by the insolence of the Barbarians, he swore he would show them that very night whether his soldiers could fly or not; in fact, he had a plan ready.

He said to his officers, "You have among your men some recruits from this part of the country. Send me three hundred shepherds. They are always able to lead their flocks anywhere and are just as nimble as their own goats."

A few hours later, the young mountaineers arrived. Such was Alexander's repute and fame that they were filled with enthusiasm and clamouring to be allowed to show him what they could do.

Without delay, Alexander addressed them in these words: "Men, look at this rock. There is only one path to the summit, and that is very well guarded, but elsewhere not a single sentry has been posted. Go off at once and find another way to get to the top of this crag. When you have succeeded, wave some white flags. On seeing them, I shall attack and divert the attention of the enemy. All you will have to do then is to make for their cave.

You will have great rewards, but for you, the greatest reward of all will be the joy of surmounting so difficult an obstacle."

The mountaineers greeted this speech with loud cheers, and set off at once to climb up the sides of the precipice. Through the ages, mountaineers have used the same tricks with equal success. These men must have taken with them light rations such as dried meat, which is neither too heavy nor too bulky but very nourishing, and perhaps, like the Scots, oatcakes.

Naturally, they armed themselves only with short swords which would not encumber their movements. Most important of all, they were equipped with the ropes and iron staples—which to-day we call pitons—essential for enterprises of this kind.

It may be difficult to climb a steep slope but, as long as there are ledges and projecting rocks to give hand- and foot-holds, ascent is not impossible. The real trouble comes when there is a smooth slab of rock to be negotiated. Here mountaineers hammer pitons into the rock so that they may pull themselves up by looping cords over them.

This is how Alexander's men must have climbed, though perhaps many of them stumbled and met their death by falling to the foot of the mountain.

Others, however, were more successful. After waiting anxiously for many hours, Alexander suddenly saw a flash of white near the summit of the rock.

There could be no doubt about it at all, for the signal was given on many other places on the height; the brave and courageous mountaineers had accomplished their mission. Now, it remained for Alexander to exploit this success. It would not be easy, for only a handful of men had reached their goal.

Once again Alexander sent for Cophes and said: "Go again to Arimazes and summon him to surrender."

When Cophes did so, the Sogdian began to laugh and jeer as he did before. How could Alexander hope to attack him with success? He told the Persian to go away quickly unless he wanted to be thrown over the side of the precipice.

"Come out of this cave," said Cophes, "and look about you. What can you see above you on the heights? You told us to go and get wings. What have you got to say now? I am leaving you, but take my advice, surrender whilst there is time."

Having said these words, Cophes went away.

Soon after, an immense clamour rose from the Macedonian camp. From below there came the incessant blaring of trumpets. What was happening? Could this be a signal for attack? Panic seized Arimazes, for he did not realise how few men were threatening him from above; indeed, it seemed to him that there was a soldier behind every rock. Overcome with fear, he decided to surrender unconditionally.

25

The King Murders his Best Friend

AUGHING, shouting, and singing, twenty men with wreaths of flowers on their heads were feasting with their lord and king, Alexander of Macedonia. The banquet was coming to an end, but a huge cup full of strong, sweet wine was being passed from hand to hand.

The king sat at the head of the table. Near to him was Clitus, a tried companion and an old friend. His sister had been Alexander's nurse, and Clitus himself had saved his master's life in battle. His kindly face was tanned by the Asian sun; he was radiant because the banquet was being given in his honour.

Clitus had just been made governor of Sogdiana and was to be left behind so that he could carry out his duties. This feasting was part of a farewell ceremony.

Alexander wore a Persian robe, a long, white, embroidered garment held in at the waist by a broad sash. Increasingly, the king found pleasure in imitating his Persian predecessors, for he now claimed to be the heir of Darius whose daughter he had married.

Whenever he came back from his warlike expeditions, he loved to relax and enjoy the pleasures provided in his sumptuous palaces, where armies of cooks provided him with exquisite meals, barbers dressed his hair with the greatest care and footmen prepared highly-scented baths for him. More and more did he withdraw from his old friends. Many of his Macedonian Companions were surprised to find that they had to obtain permission from a Persian official before they could come into the presence of their king. Often, too, he was surrounded by young Persians who had rallied to his side, and were permitted to serve in his picked guards or even govern provinces. The truth was that Alexander wished to unite the vast empire which he had conquered and, in order to do so, he encouraged his officers to marry Persian women. Many of the rough Macedonians did not sympathise with this ambition and began to be angry with their king for his friendship with their erstwhile enemies.

However, on the evening of the banquet, everyone was cheerful—rather too cheerful, for the guests had helped themselves very freely to the wine. Of course, the king was drunk, drunker than anyone else; the only sober men in the room were the Macedonian sentries who watched over the safety of their king, spear in hand.

Three or four Persian clowns arrived and climbed onto the table preparing to entertain the guests with dancing and singing. For a time, everything went with a swing, for their contortions made everybody laugh. Then, suddenly one of the clowns announced the following toast in a mocking voice: "Long life and success to the most mighty captain, Armenias of Teos."

A chill fell on the assembly. This officer was a courageous soldier, but rather elderly and his bad luck was proverbial. He only had to receive an order to go on a mission or carry out a manœuvre on the field of battle, to suffer a serious setback. Alexander was always quite ready to laugh at the misfortunes of the good old man; this evening he rocked with laughter on hearing the scurrilous jingles composed about him.

"Tell us another story," he cried. "Tell us all about Philotas of Argos who was beaten by an angry Persian husband."

This time the clown was funnier than ever but, whilst he imitated the contortions of the unfortunate Macedonian, the guests grew increasingly uneasy. They hated being reminded of occasions when the Greeks were shown to disadvantage in front of the Persians. The senior officers felt far more humiliated than their juniors, for most of the people whom the clowns made fun of were old soldiers hampered by their age or by their wounds. Clitus found these jokes more offensive than anyone else.

"You must stop all this fooling," he shouted out to Alexander, pointing at the clowns.

"Certainly not. They are very funny," answered the king. "Just listen, they are going to tell us now the story of Onesicrisces, the old officer who mistook some bags of flour for camels."

"If he took them for camels, it's because he's got bad eyesight," growled Clitus, "and if he's got bad eyesight, it's because of the burning oil thrown into his face during the siege of Tyre, and that was in your service, Alexander! Are you trying to make your own officers ridiculous in the eyes of these Persians, wretched slaves who are not fit to wipe our sandals with their beards?"

"What on earth are you talking about, Clitus? They are nothing but a lot of old fools, so old that they are beginning to be afraid of their own shadows."

"People aren't cowards, Alexander, because they are crippled or old. You have no right to jeer at them just because you are young and lucky!"

Alexander turned towards the guests and said in a jeering voice: "Clitus is trying to defend these old fools. He is even trying to call their cowardice bad luck."

This time, Clitus nearly choked with fury and, leaping to his feet, he shook his fist at the king.

"I, a coward! Was it my cowardice that saved your life even though you do think you're a son of the gods! You refuse to remember what happened at Granicus. You turned your back—yes, your back—to the sword of the Persian who was attacking you, when with my own arms I knocked it out of his hand! Where would you be Alexander, if it hadn't been for an old fool like me?"

"That's an old story, Clitus!" shouted Alexander, "everybody's heard it a hundred times; you've told it far too often."

The guests began to get restless. On these occasions, the king often quarrelled with one of his friends and he was quite ready to put up with some criticism, but Clitus caught him on some very tender spots. Was he not jeering at Alexander because the king claimed the right to be worshipped as a son of Zeus? The Macedonians often laughed about these concessions to oriental customs when they were alone. It seemed to them all right for a pharaoh or for a king of Persia to make a lot of ignorant fools believe that their father was a Sun God, but the Greeks did not fall for such nonsense.

"Son of Zeus! You were not feeling like an immortal on that day," yelled Clitus. "Son of Zeus! Do you take us for a lot of silly Persians? And now you are prepared to ignore your father—he was a great king, our noble Philip, my master and my benefactor! He fought against men and conquered them, but all his son can do is to conquer slaves, clowns and women!"

Alexander grew pale with anger. Perhaps he had suffered too much in his childhood as a result of having such a glorious father; in any case, he did not like hearing too many references to the exploits of the great Philip.

By now, the more sober of the guests tried to bring Alexander to reason. Those next to Clitus seized hold of him, tried to stop him from talking and to drag him out of the room, but he resisted and only made matters worse. "Happy are those who died before seeing the Greeks flogged by the Persians; before the Macedonians had to go on their bended knees to ask foreigners to let them see their own king. If you don't like what I have to say, don't have anything to do with free men. Invite to your banquets instead these servile Barbarians who will crouch down in front of you like a lot of slaves."

Alexander seized an apple, threw it at Clitus and, with a trembling hand, tried to find his sword; but the guards had taken the precaution of hiding it.

Thrusting back the friends who tried to calm him, he got up and called out: "I am betrayed! My friends are

12

manhandling me. I am about to be murdered like Darius! Trumpeter, sound the alarm!"

Seeing that Alexander was not in his right mind the young soldier stepped back without obeying.

In the meantime, some of the guests succeeded in dragging Clitus out of the tent. With relief, everyone thought that a very awkward situation had come to an end; now the king himself seemed to be calmer.

Suddenly Clitus appeared at the other end of the tent and once again he taunted the king with taking all the glory which his soldiers should have shared. Exasperated, Alexander snatched a lance out of the sentry's hand and, with a single movement, thrust it right through the body of Clitus who uttered a cry and fell back dead. There was a ghastly pause while all the onlookers stood still, horrified. Suddenly, the young king realised that he had killed his best friend and, picking up the lance again, he tried to throw himself upon it. The weapon was knocked out of his hand, just in time; in spite of his struggles, the Companions dragged him from the tent.

All that night and for the whole of the following day, wracked by the most terrible remorse, Alexander rolled about on the ground, tearing his garments and weeping. Sometimes he spoke of his love for Clitus, he praised his kindness, his courage, his generosity; sometimes he besought his friends not to leave him alone.

"Who can ever trust me?" he cried, "I have murdered my best friend. If any friends remain to me they are bound to fear me."

With great patience, his friends gradually succeeded in consoling him, but he never recovered altogether from the shame and sorrow of this crime. However, the Macedonians had such a great love for Alexander that they even decreed that the king had acted legally in punishing Clitus for his insolence, hoping to calm his great remorse.

Little by little, because he was young, full of life, and had so many duties to perform, so many ambitions to fulfil, the memory of his fearful crime grew dim.

Weeks passed, and then he set off once more at the head of his army. Life had begun again.

26

The Boldest Expedition of All

"COME what may," said the king to the seer Demothone, "I will advance into India."

"Lord," was the answer, "the gods have put the words into my mouth—your life is in danger."

Alexander was not in a good mood. He was overwhelmed by the heat and the damp stench of rotting vegetation. Though his ambition to reach the furthest limits of the known world was as great as ever, he felt uneasy. He was weary of these broad rivers which had to be crossed on flimsy rafts or forded perilously; he was weary also of the never-ending numbers of cotton-clad warriors who opposed his progress; and lastly, he was weary of the war elephants of his enemies which made his horses panic.

The Macedonian soldiers were beginning to fight reluctantly, completely exhausted by the intense heat and the endless marches under the burning sun or through torrential rain; the Hetairoi themselves were beginning to be hostile. Alexander felt lonely, disillusioned and anxious, he yearned to finish this campaign, to go as far as the next sea and then to return to Babylon having completed his gigantic task.

Yet, as he advanced through India, new enemies seemed to spring out of the soil every day. Rajah after rajah, covered with pearls, riding on elephants, led thousands of archers, horsemen and foot soldiers against him.

Eventually, his advance was checked by a strongly fortified city which would not surrender.

As usual, ever ready to lead his troops into the most dangerous actions, Alexander clambered up a ladder placed against the ramparts of the beleaguered city. Scarcely had he obtained a foothold on the top of the wall than the ladder behind him broke under the weight of the troops who were scaling it. So the king was left alone with three of his Companions to face a numerous enemy.

Hard-pressed, the four men defended themselves as best they could with their backs protected by the spreading branches and trunk of a tree.

Skilfully, the king manœuvred his shield to protect himself from sword-thrusts and missiles. Finally, a long, sharp arrow struck him in the chest and he staggered back, killing an Indian with a last supreme effort. At the same moment, reinforcements arrived, and two courageous Macedonians shielded the king with their bodies, though in doing so they lost their lives.

Fortunately, the assailants had scaled the walls in other places, and the besieged began to give way; the gates of the city had been forced at last.

Whilst his troops battered their way through the streets of the town to put an end to the desperate resistance of their enemies, Alexander was carried off on a shield like one of the great heroes of the Siege of Troy. It was not the first time that he had been wounded; indeed the scars of past battles marked his body in many places, but this time, the wound was a deep one.

It is said that, as his personal doctor was absent, Alexander ordered one of his officers to widen the wound with his sword so as to be able to pull out the barbed head of the arrow. Although he bled profusely, the king survived. Seven days later, when he was out of danger, he summoned enough strength to show himself to his soldiers, though his weakness was still apparent.

His officers besought him to rest to make sure that he would recover his health.

"Which of us," said one of them, "would be prepared to survive you? Watch over your safety which is the safety of us all."

27

The War God Dies in Bed

FTER his return from India, Alexander, indefatigable as ever, began to prepare for an expedition against the Arabs. He assembled in Babylon some troops who had recently been recruited in Persia and distributed them among the different regiments of his standing army. There was a pompous ceremony over which he presided, seated on the throne of the kings of Persia and surrounded by the guards of the late Darius.

As it was very hot, Alexander descended from his throne to drink, in the coolness of a tent, with members of his suite. Whilst he was doing this, a strange man of crazy appearance rushed forward and, before he could be stopped, seized the royal mantle and diadem, put them on and climbed onto the throne. He was a lunatic; but that did not make this incident any the less sinister, for the gods often lead the weak in mind to show mortals what the future holds in store. Certainly the seers regarded this as an evil omen.

"Alexander will soon be replaced by a stranger," they said.

Nevertheless, the king continued his preparations to attack Arabia. He gave a banquet in honour of his friend Nearchus, the admiral of the fleet, who was to command the naval forces of the expedition. It was late and he was about to retire, when friends invited him to go on celebrating. Although very tired, the king accepted, and the night of heavy drinking was a great strain on his health.

The next morning after a bath, he felt feverish and went to sleep again. On the morrow, he insisted on taking part in the usual sacrifices, but was carried on a litter as far as the altars. He had to go to bed for the rest of the day. In the evening, making a great effort, he got up and summoned his officers. It was excessively warm, for in the month of June in Babylonia the heat is intense, there are flies and mosquitoes everywhere and the turgid waters of the rivers give out a vile stench. In the evening, he ordered his bearers to carry him down to the water's edge in the hopes of finding a fresh breeze.

The fourth day passed fairly well, but he was attacked by fever again at night; on the sixth day it was worse than ever. Nevertheless, the king continued to give orders to his officers and to his administrators, although his condition grew worse. On the ninth day, he summoned his generals, but though he recognised them, he was not able to speak to them.

As the news of his illness had spread throughout the army, the Greek soldiers gathered round the gates of the palace, hoping to hear that their beloved leader was recovering.

At last, the gates were opened and some of these men

were allowed to file past the king's bed. Since he could not even speak, all that he could do was to greet his faithful warriors by a slight flickering of his eyelids. In despair, some of his close friends took a desperate measure to bring about his recovery. Since they had lost confidence in their own gods, they went to the sanctuary of a Babylonian god to consult his Oracle.

"Must we bring the king to your temple?" they asked anxiously.

The Oracle replied: "Let him stay where he is, he will be better there."

Alas! There was no change in the sick man's condition. A few hours later, on the evening of 13th June, 323 B.C. Alexander died. He was thirty-three years old. This was indeed a sad end for a king who had so many times faced a glorious and heroic death on the field of battle.

Clearly, he had never considered the possibility of death, for he had taken no care to ensure the succession of the vast empire which he had conquered. He had no children when he died, though a son was born to his wife shortly after his death. As his wife was a Sogdian and the Greeks would not submit to anyone of mixed blood, the empire of Alexander came to an end at the same time as the great man who had created it.

There is an eastern proverb which says that when the lion dies, the hyenas fight over his carcass. Thus it was that Alexander's empire was divided up by his generals who fought each other for the largest share.